STO

FRIENDS
OF ACPL

W9-CZX-094

Fourteen Hundred Cowries

Fourteen Hundred Cowries

AND OTHER AFRICAN TALES

Collected by Abayomi Fuja

With an introduction by Anne Pellowski

Illustrated by Ademola Olugebefola

Lothrop, Lee & Shepard Company, New York

First American edition 1971

Text copyright © 1962 by Oxford University Press

Illustrations copyright © 1971 by Ademola Olugebefola

British edition published in 1962 under the title
Fourteen Hundred Cowries: Traditional Stories of the Yoruba.

All rights reserved • No part of this book may be reproduced or
utilized in any form or by any means, electronic or mechanical,
including photocopying, recording or by any information
storage and retrieval system, without permission in writing
from the Publisher • Inquiries should be addressed to
Lothrop, Lee and Shepard Company, 105 Madison Ave.,

New York, N. Y. 10016 • Printed in the United States of America

Library of Congress Catalog Card Number 79-142811

CO. SCHOOLS

C772658

Contents

Introduction

Recently, I read again an essay on storytelling I had used many times in my courses. In it, I came upon the statement, "Storytelling today has been kept alive by a few storytellers," and the article then named Marie Shedlock, Gudrun Thorne-Thomsen, Ruth Sawyer, and Frances Clarke Sayers, among others.

I began to wonder whether, on the many previous occasions when I had read and used that article, I had added silently the phrase "in the United States," or whether I really could have been so chauvinistic as to believe that our modest efforts to keep oral narration alive in this country rank higher in importance than the storytelling of traditional societies in Africa, Asia, and Latin America. It is among peoples in those parts of the world that storytelling is truly a living, breathing art.

At first, one is puzzled as to why this narrow view has stayed with us so long. We have had literally thousands of collections of folk tales for children from all over the world. In short, if one searches for printed proof of interest in storytelling, and the tales to tell, it is there—for a hundred and more countries. And yet, it is perhaps because of these very collections that we tend to think we have a monopoly on storytelling. Most of them have been edited by American or European writers and in all too many instances there is no information about the sources, the methods, and techniques of telling, the "why" behind the tales. The language has been changed to suit our children and elements that are disturbing to our culture are deleted. Yet the tales are duly labeled "African" or "Asian" or with some more specific cultural adjective, and they are used to introduce our children to those cultures.

Fourteen Hundred Cowries is a long overdue answer to this problem. Abayomi Fuja recorded these tales several decades ago, but it has taken us until this decade to find them and publish them for an American audience. Although the language has many Anglicisms due to Mr. Fuja's training in British missionary schools, the spirit of the Yoruba storyteller shines through. He has kept many of the phrases in a kind of free verse, in the tradition of the original lines, which were usually chanted.

The Yoruba are one of the most numerous of the West African tribes. There are estimated to be more than five million members living mainly in Western Nigeria. They have been noted for centuries for their great musical and story- or speech-making talents. Some of the finest "talking drummers" are Yorubas, who succeed in squeezing and coaxing out of their variously shaped and individually named drums a "language" that closely resembles Yoruba speech patterns.

Stories and songs can be either traditional or spontaneous in Yoruba. They can be memorized and passed on orally from generation to generation with virtually no change. Or, like some of the "praise" songs and stories, they can be composed on the spur of the moment to honor some person or event, and then be refined and changed later, even to the extent of making the "praise" tone a rather acerbic one!

8

The storyteller or teacher using this collection should become as familiar as possible with the sound of the Yoruba language, with their music and drumming. (Folkways has a number of recordings of both songs and drumming of the Yoruba.) It is entirely in keeping with Yoruba storytelling practice to change lines or actions to suit one's personal style, but this should not be done in contradiction to the basic patterns of Yoruba sound and rhythm.

A good example is the title story. My personal preference would be to always use the phrase "you are in trouble" at the end of the first line of each cumulation. I would use other phrases describing the animals, objects, plants, and persons also in repetition, rather than changing them with each verse. I might chant the verses, using a strong rhythm and possibly drum accompaniment. On the other hand, the little verse in the story "The Boy and the Piece of Yam" seems so perfect in its simplicity that I would not change a word. Other storytellers might find they preferred to do just the opposite.

These tales may be told for the sheer enjoyment of the stories, or as one African way of explaining the actions of men and beasts, or to teach a moral in the Yoruba manner. When one can tell them with the perfect fusion of all three of these purposes, one is close to being a Yoruba storyteller.

Anne Pellowski, director
Information Center on Children's Cultures
U.S. Committee for UNICEF

Fourteen Hundred Cowries

There once lived a cricket who wished to marry. Unfortunately he had no money with which to pay his father-in-law the dowry. The cricket therefore went to a certain moneylender, who was also a palm wine seller, and borrowed fourteen hundred cowries. Instead of taking the money to his father-in-law, he spent it on palm wine, with the result that he soon became very drunk. Resting awhile against a cotton tree, he slipped, and a thorn on the bark pricked him. He started to sing:

> O cotton tree, O cotton tree—there is trouble,
> For, you see, your thorns have pricked my poor
> body.
> The cricket who owes the palm wine man is
> your brother,
> Fourteen hundred cowries is the debt you owe
> to me,
> The gods will be angry if you do not pay up.

The cotton tree bent its young leaves in the

breeze, and a passing roan ate some of them.
The cotton tree started to sing:

> Beautiful roan, beautiful roan, you are in trou-
> ble,
> You have eaten my leaves as they bent in the
> breeze.
> Cricket's body was wounded by cotton tree's
> thorns,
> The cricket who owes the palm wine seller the
> cowries.
> Fourteen hundred of these you must pay unto
> me,
> The gods will be angry if you do not pay up.

As the roan paused to eat the leaves, he was
wounded by a hunter's arrow. The roan started
to sing:

Hunter, for shooting a roan there is trouble
    for you,
See, you have wounded the roan who ate cotton
    tree's leaves.
I have eaten those leaves as they bent in the
    breeze.
Cricket's body was wounded by cotton tree's
    thorns,
Drunken cricket owes the wine seller a debt.
Fourteen hundred cowries, fourteen hundred
    cowries,
The gods will be angry if you do not pay up.

As the hunter shot at the roan, he stumbled over
an old tree stump. Then the hunter started to
sing:

Stump of wood, stump of wood, there is trou-
    ble for you,
For your clumsy shape was the cause of my
    stumble.
You made me wound the roan as he ate the
    green branch,
Green branch of cotton tree, whose thorns
    pricked the cricket.
The cricket from the wine man first borrowed
    the cowries,
He spent them on palm wine. His debt is now
    yours.
One thousand and four hundred shells is the
    debt,
The gods will be angry if you do not pay up.

By the stump of wood grew a mushroom, and a

woman came and picked the mushroom. The stump of wood started to sing:

Old woman, old woman, your act has brought
    trouble,
You have picked a fine mushroom that grew by
    my stump,
And the stump was the cause of the hunter's
    stumble,
For he wounded the roan as he ate the green
    leaves.
The leaves of the tree that wounded the cricket.
Cricket started the debt by owing the cowries,
When drunk, to the wine man, and now it's your
    debt.
Cowries one thousand four hundred it will cost
    you;
The gods will be angry if you do not pay up.

The old woman went home with her mushroom, and as she entered her compound, one of her hens pecked her foot, hoping to get some of the mushroom, and she started to cry:

O my hen, O my hen—this has brought you
    much trouble.
Who taught you to greet me by pecking my
    foot?
My trouble came from a mushroom at the stump
    of a tree.
The stump troubled the hunter when shooting
    the roan.
The roan was in trouble for eating green leaves,

14

Green leaves on the tree that wounded the
    cricket.
Then more trouble for cricket in debt to the
    wine man,
Trouble when drunk and in debt through the
    wine,
Four hundred and one thousand cowries is my
    price.
The gods will be angry if you do not pay up.

As the hen pecked the woman's foot, a passing
hawk caught sight of the hen's chickens and
swooping down, carried one away. The hen
started to squawk:

Hawk, hawk, you will find that this day has
    brought you much trouble,
You have stolen a chicken and carried him off.
And I greeted the woman by pecking her foot.
She had picked a mushroom and annoyed a tree
    stump,
The stump tripped a hunter as he shot at a
    roan;
Then the roan ate the leaves of the tree with
    thorns,
And those were the thorns that pricked the
    drunk cricket.
The cricket is in debt to a palm wine seller,
And to his father-in-law this debt should have
    gone,
One thousand and four hundred cowries you
    will bring;
The gods will be angry if you do not pay up.

15

The hawk, as he flew away with the chicken, dropped one of his tail feathers. A woman who happened to be passing with her child, stopped to pick it up. The hawk saw her do this and started to sing:

> Woman with baby, this day brings you trouble,
> You have stolen a feather that grew in my tail,
> I have stolen a chicken and carried him off,
> The chicken of the hen who pecked the woman's foot.
> A mushroom was plucked by the woman near a stump,
> And the hunter's fall was caused by the stump,
> That was the hunter who wounded a feeding roan.
> The roan it was who angered the tree with the thorns.
> The cricket who owed the cowries was injured by the tree. He was drunk at the time of the debt.
> Twice seven hundred cowries is the price that you owe.
> The gods will be angry if you do not pay up.

The woman with the baby, after she had picked up her feather, was careless with her baby. It fell from her back and started to cry. The king's drummer who happened to be passing at the time was angry with her and beat her. Then the woman started to yell:

> King's drummer, king's drummer, this day brings you trouble.

16

Oh, why should you beat me and cause me this
pain?
See here is the feather I took from the hawk.
He dropped it as he carried the young chicken
off.
Its parent was the hen who pecked the old
woman,
When from a tree stump she had stolen a mush-
room.
The old stump had caused the hunter to slip,
He shot at the roan as it ate the green leaves,
The poor cricket was pricked by the cotton
tree's thorns,
The poor cricket who started the trouble by
debt.
For all the dowry money, when drunk he mis-
spent.
Fourteen hundred cowries I am asking from
you;
The gods will be angry if you do not pay up.

The king's son happened to see the drummer
beating the woman, and he was very angry and
beat the drummer too. As he beat him, the
drummer started to wail:

O prince, if you beat me the gods will bring
trouble.
Spare me, I beg you, and I will serve you for-
ever.
I saw this bad woman ill-treating her baby,
I saw the evil hawk stealing a hen's chicken,
I saw the vicious hen pecking a poor woman,
I saw the stump's mushroom stolen by her,

17

18

I saw the tree stump destroy the hunter's shot,
I saw the wounded roan stealing from the cot-
   ton tree,
I saw the sharpened thorn pierce the cricket's
   body,
I saw the drunken cricket start the trouble,
For he owes for his wife and he owes for the
   wine;
O prince, fourteen hundred is not much to ask,
The gods will be angry if you do not pay up.

When the prince had finished beating his father's drummer, he went directly to his father,
the king, and the prince sang:

O father, this day has brought us much trouble,
Many of your subjects are greatly in debt.
First I owe your drummer fourteen hundred
   cowries,
The drummer owes the woman fourteen hun-
   dred too,
The woman owes the hawk fourteen hundred
   also.
Then this hawk is in debt to a hen for the same.
Then a woman is asking this sum from a hen,
Fourteen hundred cowries the woman owes to
   a stump,
Then a hunter's demanding the same from the
   stump,
And the hunter's in debt to a roan for as much.
Fourteen hundred more, the roan owes the tree,
The same compensation the tree owes to a
   cricket,

The cricket wants this sum to pay a palm wine
man,
Fourteen hundred cowries, and we are all in
debt.
The gods will be angry if we do not pay up.

The king said nothing as he listened to his son,
then, getting up and going to his treasury, he
withdrew fourteen hundred cowries. These he
gave to his son, and as he took the money the
king sang in a shaking voice:

O son, as you say, this trouble is great.
From my treasury funds we surely must pay.
Many of my subjects are heavily in debt.
First fourteen hundred to you for the drummer.
Then the drummer pays the woman this money.
The woman passes on the cowries to the hawk,
The hawk must pay the money to the hen,
Next the hen will pay the cowries to the woman,
And the woman must pass the money to the
stump,
Then the stump will hand it over to the hunter.
This money the hunter will give to the wounded
roan,
The roan must pay the debt to the cotton tree,
And the cotton tree owes these cowries to the
cricket,
If the cricket isn't drunk, he pays the wine
seller.
O fourteen hundred cowries from my treasury,
The gods will be angry if we do not pay up.

Everybody carried out the king's wishes, and

by the time the fourteen hundred cowries had been given to the cricket by the cotton tree, he had completely recovered himself. He paid the palm wine seller the fourteen hundred cowries he owed him for all the palm wine he had drunk. Then he borrowed the same amount back again and set out to pay his father-in-law the dowry money.

The Wrestling Contest Between the Cat and the Tortoise

In the Country of the Animals, the cat was regarded as the champion wrestler of all the animals, for he had so far managed to throw everybody who had challenged him. It was, therefore, not surprising that he enjoyed great popularity, and his friendship was eagerly sought after.

One day, the tortoise came to call on the cat and invited him to visit him and accept his hospitality. Now the cat had been warned that the tortoise was a very clever and sly person, so when the tortoise invited him to his home, he did not want to go. He made excuses and put off the visit. The tortoise was far from snubbed by the cat's refusal, and continued to press his unwanted friendship.

At last the cat, more for the sake of peace and quiet than for friendship's sake, agreed to visit the tortoise. When he arrived he was surprised, for the tortoise had prepared a large and very fine fish and plenty of palm wine, fufu, and kola nuts. Now the cat was very fond of all these things and he sat down beside his host and enjoyed the feast. Having eaten to satisfaction, he lay down and stretched himself out under the shade of some large, cool banana leaves, thinking sleepily to himself that the tortoise was not such a bad fellow after all, and that the reports about him had been incorrect.

After this the two animals became close friends and were often to be seen seated under the shade of the banana leaves in the tortoise's compound.

One day, some little time after this, the tortoise suddenly asked the cat how he had managed to become a champion wrestler and throw

animals that appeared to be so much stronger than himself. "Ah," said the cat, "you see I have a powerful juju which I use when I wrestle: in this way I am able to throw all comers. It is very easy indeed."

"Tell me, my friend," replied the tortoise, "how many jujus you have, and what they are. Perhaps I am seeking for too much information, but I am very interested in your great powers, and I am your friend."

"That is very easy," answered the cat. "I am willing to tell you. I have two jujus that I use," and the cat related what they were. Now the cat was very clever and not such a fool as the tortoise imagined, for in actual fact he used three jujus for his wrestling contests. He did not tell the tortoise about the third one.

Some time later, all the animals were very surprised indeed to learn that the tortoise had taken up wrestling. At first they laughed a lot at the idea of a tortoise wrestling, but as the tortoise continued to win contest after contest against all comers, their surprise and admiration grew. Meanwhile, the cat watched with great amusement, but said nothing.

As the tortoise defeated each comer, his conceit grew, until the day came that the cat had been waiting for.

"Why don't you challenge the cat?" said all the tortoise's supporters. "You are now the strongest animal amongst us, and the cat has been successful for ages and we have noticed that he has not challenged anybody for a long time. Now is your chance to become the champion wrestler in the land of the animals. Try throwing the cat."

"Yes," replied the conceited animal, "now I will throw the cat and make him acknowledge me as the champion wrestler in the land. Go and arrange a day for the contest."

On the day appointed, there was a great concourse of animals gathered and much excitement and talk on the merits and chances of both contestants. An open space was marked off and the animals sat down outside to watch what promised to be the most interesting wrestling match ever held, for neither side had ever been defeated.

In the first bout both the cat and the tortoise used the first juju, and after a great struggle, a draw was announced.

In the second bout the animals used the second juju, and another great tussle ensued, without either animal overcoming the other. This too was declared a draw.

The tortoise now suggested that they should

26

share the championship between them, but all the animals called out for a third and final bout to settle the matter.

Having no more jujus, the tortoise decided to use a combination of the first and second juju. The cat, of course, used his third juju, with the result that the tortoise was soundly beaten. And ever afterwards the tortoise has taken good care to avoid both the cat and the wrestling ring.

If you have a friend do not try to fight him even if you think you know his secrets.

Concerning the Leopard
and the Hedgehog

In the beginning, there lived a certain hedgehog in the Country of the Animals. This hedgehog was on very friendly terms with a leopard and was always having to help him out of small difficulties. The leopard never failed to call on the hedgehog for assistance when he encountered trouble, which happened very frequently. The hedgehog, on the other hand, was a most reliable animal and took great care both of himself and his family. The two animals lived apart, the leopard in the forest and the hedgehog among the tall grass on the edge of the farms. Although the hedgehog seldom went into the forest, the leopard was often to been seen prowling around through the long grass near the farms.

One day during the harmattan, the farmers began preparing some new ground for farming, the old farmland having been exhausted. When they had cut down the thick undergrowth, the farmers proceeded to burn it, with the result that the fire soon spread to the tall grass that

surrounded the old farms. The hedgehog was able to save his wife and their three children, but not his house, which was quickly destroyed by the fire.

Homeless, they fled towards the forest for safety, and on reaching the damp, green undergrowth, the hedgehog and his family rested. It was then that the hedgehog remembered the number of times that he had helped the leopard in the past, so he decided to ask the leopard if he could stay with him until such time as he had rebuilt his home. He called his eldest son and told him to go and inform the leopard of their plight, and ask if he could provide them with food and shelter.

The young hedgehog went to the leopard's

home and informed him of their loss and asked for food and shelter. But the leopard was a very dangerous and unpleasant animal, and had only pretended to live on friendly terms with the hedgehog for what he could get out of him. Now, thought the leopard, the hedgehog will be of no further use to me. So he sent back a very rude message to the hedgehog saying, "Come along, and eat and be eaten." In this way, he thought, "I will provide a living place for the hedgehog and his family forever!"

When the young hedgehog took back this terrible news, his father realized what an ungrateful friend the leopard had turned out to be. Not only could he not be relied upon as a friend, but obviously in the future the hedgehogs would have to protect themselves from the leopard and all his family.

The leopard had followed the young hedgehog back to see where they all were, knowing perfectly well that they would not come to his home to be eaten. When he saw the hedgehog's family moving away, he came bounding after them. There seemed little hope for the hedgehog family, for in a few strides the leopard would have caught them. Fortunately, however, an old, disused anthill stood close by and the hedgehog, seeing a small entrance, quickly pushed his

family inside, and skipped in himself, and so was able to escape from the leopard as he came bounding up.

The hedgehog was so pleased with the new home necessity had forced him to occupy, and its safety from fires and leopards, that forever afterwards the hedgehog family have been very fond of living in holes in the ground and in old anthills. And ever since that time they have had nothing to do with leopards.

The Beautiful Girl and the Fish

In the far-off days when there was great magic everywhere, there lived a beautiful girl. Many young men of her town wished to marry her, but she had refused all offers, saying that her husband must be the most handsome man in all the land. One day, as she was busy in the marketplace, she saw a very handsome man and immediately fell in love with him. Going up to him, she told him how attracted she was by his looks, and that she wished to become his wife.

"I should very much like to have you as my wife, but unfortunately I am not a man, and am not of your people, for I come from the river at Idunmaibo. You see, I am a fish, and when I am not living in the water, the gods have given me the power to turn myself into a young man, but my home is the river and to the river I must return," replied the stranger.

"It matters not," replied the girl. "You may be fish or man, but I still love you. If you prom-

ise to come forth from the water from time to time, and see me as you are now, I will gladly marry you."

"So be it then," replied the fish-man, and he led the girl to Idunmaibo and they went to a certain place on the river bank. "Here is my home," said the fish-man. "Whenever you want me, come to this place and sing the magic song I will teach you." Then the young fish-man sang:

O beautiful fish of the river,
May I look through the flowing waters?
Through the surface of the river I will see you.
O lovely river that looks like silver and gems
With palace beneath, more lovely
Than the palace of kings of men.

Then the fish-man plunged into the water and was lost from sight. Every day the girl prepared some sweetmeats for her lover and taking them to Idunmaibo, she sang the magic song and the fish came to the surface. He changed into a man, climbed the bank and spent some time with his wife. He used to bring with him coral and many gems from the river and supply her with all she needed. They were very happy together and loved each other very much.

One day, the girl's parents asked her if there was anybody she wished to marry. She replied that she had a husband, but that she could not disclose his identity at present. They were very puzzled with this answer and watched her as she prepared her husband's food and carried it away. Her small brother had asked her several times if he could accompany her and carry the food, but she told him she must go alone and nobody must follow her. This answer only aroused the boy's curiosity, and he made up his mind to follow her and see where she went and what she did with the food. By means of magic, he turned himself into a fly and followed his sister to Idunmaibo and the banks of the river. Here he heard her sing the magic song and saw the fish come out of the river and turn into a man. And so he learned the words of the magic song. When they had eaten their food, the fish-

34

man said good-bye to his wife and jumped back into the water. The little boy then flew home, and changing into a boy, he went straight to his parents and told them what he had witnessed, and that his sister had married a fish.

The girl's father and mother were very angry when they heard the boy's story. But they decided not to say anything about the matter to their daughter on her return. Instead it was arranged that she should be sent to her father's people for a couple of days while they decided what to do. So the girl was sent away, much to her grief, for her father's people dwelled far away and she would not be able to visit her husband during her absence.

When the girl had departed, her father told the boy to lead him to Idunmaibo and sing the magic song on the riverbank. When they reached the spot, the boy, imitating his sister's voice, sang the song and the fish came out of the water. The father was waiting close by and as the fish-man climbed the bank the father killed him with his hatchet and threw him into the water. As the fish-man died he turned back slowly into a fish. C772658 CO. SCHOOLS

"I will punish my daughter for this wicked deed," shouted the father and he ordered his son to pull out the dead fish and carry it home. The fish was then dried and kept for the girl's

return. Two days later she returned, happy to
be back close to the river and her husband
again. She was anxious to leave her father's
compound and visit the river, only her father
ordered her to sit down and eat some food before she left.

"Your mother has prepared some fish for
you," he said.

"I am not hungry, Father, and I do not wish
to eat fish," the girl replied.

"You will do as I order you, girl. Sit down and
eat," said her father.

So the girl sat down with a sigh and ate the
fish. As she ate, she was startled to hear her
small brother singing softly to himself. Before
he had finished the words of his song, the bowl
of food had dropped from the girl's hands and
she sat quietly staring in front of her. The boy
repeated his song:

> How wretched it is for women to eat their hus-
> band's flesh,
> When they have taken their husbands as their
> most beloved,
> For during their absence their husbands have
> been taken out
> As a fine fish from the river for the family's
> food.

The girl, on hearing this terrible song, ran out of her father's compound and going quickly to the river bank, she sang the magic song, but her husband did not come. Then the girl sang:

> Oluweri, Oluweri, Goddess of the River,
> I have now returned with eyes of silver and hair like stars.
> Oh, if it be that my husband is dead,
> Let the face of the river run blood red,
> Or if my husband yet lives, let him come to the surface,
> There he will behold his loved one they sent cruelly away.

At that instant, the surface of the water turned blood red and the girl knew then that her parents had killed her husband. She jumped into the river, and instead of being drowned, she sank down into the river waters and became an *onijegi*.[1] And people say that even today an *onijegi* can sometimes be heard singing softly at Idunmaibo.

[1] *Onijegi*—a mermaid.

The Sad Story of the Tadpole

The king of the frogs had died, and after the funeral ceremonies were over, the question arose as to who should succeed him. All the important frog families had gathered together to select the new king, and there were many claims to the vacant throne. As a result there was much bickering, croaking, and bad feeling between the rival families. In this way the frogs spent a great deal of time in discussion without reaching any agreement, so it was proposed to consult a powerful oracle held sacred by the frogs. If they could not decide amongst themselves, then it would have to be left to the oracle to decide.

In due course, through the medium of the oracle, a certain young tadpole came to be chosen as the new king of the frogs. Nobody was more surprised and pleased at this unusual choice than the young tadpole himself. Before dispersing, the frog families decided to crown the tadpole in seven days' time as their new king.

This sudden success went to the young tadpole's head. Many frogs who had never bothered to notice him before began to gather round and flatter him. The young tadpole was so pleased with all this flattery and attention that he decided to hold a great celebration during the seven days that were to elapse before his coronation. All his new friends were invited to attend, and the finest drummers, dancers, and musicians throughout the frog world were summoned to perform. A great feast was prepared of palm-oil chop, with plenty of fufu, and many animals were slaughtered. Large pots of palm wine were placed in the tadpole's compound, and also in the streets and marketplace for the

people to drink from. All was given over to feasting and merrymaking, and no work was done throughout the country of the frogs. As was their custom, the frogs danced through the streets in the evening and on the sixth day, the tadpole, who was by now very drunk indeed, followed the procession as usual.

Determined to be the center of attraction all the time, he declared that he could dance better than any of the professional dancers. So the young tadpole danced and hopped about through the streets, and because everybody applauded him and because he was very drunk, he thought that his performance was the finest that had ever been seen in the frog world. In actual fact he could not jump and hop about properly, and kept slipping and falling over everybody that came near him, and falling over the ruts and drains in the streets. Near the marketplace there was a large refuse dump. Here the drunken tadpole came to grief, for, in trying to jump across it, he slipped down a hole and broke one of his tiny slender legs. The people placed him on a board and carried him back to his house and there the young tadpole lay in great pain, while he wondered which of the two, his leg or his head, troubled him most.

There was a law in the country of the frogs

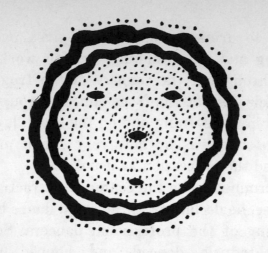

that ruled that any person suffering from a deformity could not be crowned king of the frogs. When, on the following day, the important frog families gathered together for the coronation, those frogs who were not satisfied with the oracle's choice, and those who were disgusted with the excess of the seven days' celebration, were not slow to come together and point out that the young tadpole was no longer eligible for the position, because of his broken leg.

So the young tadpole was never crowned. In his place, they chose an old toad as the new king of the frogs.

When you hear of a good thing coming your way, take care of yourself.

The Boy and the Piece of Yam

There was once a Yoruba boy who was born
with a piece of magic yam in his hand. It was
small enough to fit into his tiny palm. As the boy
grew, the yam remained with him, but it did not
grow as the boy did. Because it was a magic
piece of yam and had appeared in such a
strange manner, the boy always kept it by him,
and it remained fresh and never seemed to
wither.

One day the boy was sent by his parents to
fetch firewood from the bush. He collected the
wood and while he tied it up, he placed the tiny
piece of yam on a fallen tree trunk nearby.
Then, placing the wood on his head, he set out
for home, forgetting his piece of magic yam.

Now the animals of the bush had heard of the
boy born with the magic yam in his hand, and
while he had been cutting the wood, they had
hidden in the grass and bushes round about and
had watched him. They saw him place the yam
on the fallen tree.

When the boy had departed, they came out of their hiding places and gazed with much interest at the piece of yam. "This yam must contain a powerful juju and is worth possessing," said the leopard, and all the animals were anxious to possess it. A quarrel soon arose over who should take the yam.

Before the boy reached his parents' house, he remembered the piece of yam, and placing the bundle of firewood by the side of the path, he ran back as fast as he could to the fallen tree. When he got there, he was very surprised and frightened to see so many wild animals surrounding the tree. The boy was confused and did not know what to do. At last he decided to sing, and so distract the attention of the animals from the yam:

> My little yam—my little yam,
> Oh I forgot you in the bush.
> My mother warned me not to leave you about,
> My father warned me to keep you in my hand,
> Yet I go and forget my yam,
> My little yam, my little yam.

The boy had a very sweet voice and the animals were fascinated by his little song. They made him sing it over and over again. Soon some began drumming, and then they all joined in and danced and sang his song, and in their excite-

44

ment they forgot the magic yam. The boy gradually moved closer to the fallen tree, and when the animals were not looking, he picked up the yam and hid it in his clothes. By this time the animals were so engrossed in their dance that they did not notice the boy slip quietly away.

"Where is that boy, and who has taken the magic yam?" said the leopard, suddenly stopping in the middle of the dance. This brought the dancing, drumming, and singing to an abrupt end. All the animals stopped and gazed at the fallen tree.

"Who has taken the magic yam, and where has that singing boy gone?" demanded the leopard again in an angry voice.

"We are all fools, the boy of course has taken it. By singing to us he was able to take it unnoticed," replied the elephant.

"He must be stopped before he reaches the town and we must get hold of the yam. You run after him, elephant, and bring him back," said the leopard.

"I shall do no such thing. The suggestion is yours and you can bring him back," said the elephant in an indignant voice, and threw up his great trunk and shook his head slowly up and down.

"That settles it then; I will go myself and

fetch him back, and the magic yam becomes mine," replied the leopard hurriedly. Then, before anybody could reply, he ran off quickly in the direction of the town.

The boy, in the meantime, had run quickly home, not bothering to pick up his bundle of sticks as he passed. He told his mother the story concerning the dancing animals and their interest in the magic yam.

Now the boy's mother, like many other Yoruba women, employed herself by dyeing cloth. When she heard her son's story she greatly feared the animals would come to the house and harm her son, so calling her servants and warning them to keep a sharp lookout, she armed them all with the dye sticks that were stained with the deep blue marks of the indigo dye.

Sure enough, it was not long before the leopard found his way to the house, and with a great snarl he rushed into the compound. The next minute he found himself a prisoner surrounded by hostile people, all bearing big sticks dripping with indigo dye. Somebody had closed the door behind him. Then they all started to beat and prod him unmercifully, till all his body was stained with marks from the indigo. At last he managed to escape over the compound wall and reach the safety of the bush.

Since that day, all leopards have carried the marks of the dye sticks on their bodies, and no animal has gone looking for magic yams in the towns of men.

Oni and the Great Bird

There was once a strange boy called Oni who was born wearing a pair of boots. As Oni grew the boots grew also. When he was a boy of eighteen years of age, war broke out between his people and another village. It was during the battle that Oni made a second discovery about himself, which separated him from his fellow men and made him different. The enemy arrows did not seem to harm him. Many pierced his body which in the ordinary course of events should have slain him. The other young men noticed this too. They already regarded Oni as strange because of his wonderful boots, but when they discovered that he could not be killed they were afraid to have him near them. When he returned from the war, several people tried to kill him in various ways, but without any success. Finding this did not work, it was decided to find an excuse to banish him. He was accused of setting a house on fire in the village, and al-

though Oni had nothing to do with the fire, he was found guilty and banished.

Oni wandered alone on foot for a long time. One afternoon he came to the banks of a great river and finding an empty canoe and feeling tired of walking, he got into the boat and made his way downstream. Towards evening, when it was growing dark, Oni reached a town, and decided to pull into the bank and spend the night there. There were the sounds of many bells being rung and people seemed to be in a hurry. Oni tied up the canoe and climbed the bank, and as he did so he met an old man. "Good evening, my friend. My name is Oni. I am a stranger to your town and have nowhere to spend the night.

Will you take me to your house?" Oni asked the old man.

"Yes, certainly, come along with me, but we must go quickly because the bells are ringing and it is growing dusk," replied the old man.

"What is the name of your town and why do your people ring bells on the approach of darkness?" asked Oni.

"People call this place Ajo, but hurry up, we must get indoors. I will explain the bells to you when we are inside," replied the old man.

When they reached the old man's house, they found his people waiting anxiously for him at the door. The bells had now stopped ringing and they were hurried inside and the door was securely fastened.

"Now," said the old man, "sit down and eat with us and I will explain. For many years now we, the people of Ajo, have been troubled by the nightly arrival of a giant eagle. We call it Anodo. It always appears on the approach of darkness and stays until the approach of dawn. Anybody who is unfortunate enough to be out of doors at the time of its appearance is sure to be killed by it. You were very fortunate, young man, to reach Ajo before darkness. Our king has ordered the ringing of bells to warn the people to return to their homes and lock the doors. None of us knows where the eagle comes from, or where it goes when it leaves us at dawn. It is a terrible curse and in the past it has killed many of our people."

The old man had hardly finished speaking before Oni heard the sound of great wings flapping over the house. It sounded like a great wind, and the windows and doors shook in their frames.

"It must be a very great bird," remarked Oni. After Oni had fed, the old man gave him a mat and a cloth and he lay down to sleep in the corner of the room. Sleep would not come to Oni, however, for he heard the constant noise of the great eagle's wings as it flew to and fro over Ajo.

When morning had come and the eagle had departed, Oni thanked the old man for his kindness and set out to find the King of Ajo and to ask for an audience. It was granted.

"My name is Oni and I am a stranger to your town. I have come to offer my services in helping to rid this town of the eagle Anodo," said Oni.

"And what makes you think you will succeed where so many others have tried and failed?" asked the king.

"I have certain powers and juju," said Oni.

51

"So had the others. One by one all my hunters have tried and have been killed or carried off by Anodo. Strangers have come from time to time to offer their services, but they too have perished. It is some time now since anybody has tried to kill Anodo, and I have issued orders to my remaining hunters not to try, as enough of them have been killed already," said the king.

"Have you ever offered a reward to anybody who could succeed in killing the bird?" asked Oni.

"Indeed yes. The man who succeeds will have half my kingdom. I made that offer long ago," replied the king.

"Then I will try tonight," answered Oni, and he paid his respects to the king and departed.

Oni returned to the old man's house and told him what had happened, and of his intention to challenge Anodo. The old man was very frightened and implored him to give up the idea, for he would only perish and perhaps all those in the house too. But Oni was not frightened. He took his bow and arrows and knives and examined them carefully.

It seemed ages to Oni before he heard the bells ringing. Never had he known a longer day in his life. The old man was uneasy and his people were almost hostile towards Oni. When they heard the bells ringing at last, they lost no time in fastening the doors and windows and ordered Oni to lie down on his mat and keep quiet.

Presently they heard the noise of a great wind which heralded the approach of Anodo. Soon the great wings were above the house. Oni waited till the great bird was overhead and then he commenced to sing:

Tonight Oni will be at war with Anodo,
The eagle, whose talons are sharper than knives,
For now the knives of nature and man will
    meet.
Oni is invincible; his knife is sharp.

Anodo heard the challenge as he hovered over the house, and circling slowly round he came back and sang:

53

Ah fortune, I have found a victim tonight,
I have lived many months without a kill,
Will the singer come out and feel the sharpness
Of my talons and of my beak? It will take me
A moment to tear him to pieces. Come out.

All the people in the house were terrified. They seized Oni and threw him out of the house, fearing the vengeance of Anodo on them all.

As they threw Oni out into the road, Anodo swooped down and seizing him in his talons drew him upwards. Oni slashed the eagle in the chest with his knife and the eagle dropped him with a scream. Oni fell to the ground, dazed. He picked himself up as the huge bird descended once again. He had time to use his bow and discharge an arrow into Anodo before the wounded bird beat him to the ground with his great wings and pecked him severely. Again Oni's knife tore at the eagle, and he buried it twice in Anodo. Slowly the eagle beat his great wings and rose slowly into the air; then he hovered for a last terrible dive on Oni. Oni watched him and, putting an arrow in his bow, took aim. The great bird hovered, then with a terrible noise he tore down on the boy, gathering speed as he came. There was a great roar of wind as he came down. Oni discharged a second arrow,

then another and another in quick succession, but still the bird came on. A moment later it had hit Oni and knocked him over. The boy rolled over, a thousand lights dancing before his eyes; then all went blank, and he felt himself sinking down and down into a bottomless pit. He was knocked unconscious and had not seen that the great bird was already dead before it struck him. Its great wings swept the boy to one side, and it plunged on into a cotton tree, which snapped like a twig, and came crashing down to bury the eagle and Oni under a mass of leaves.

When Oni recovered, he felt very weak, and it was all he could do to free himself from the great wing of the dead Anodo and the cotton tree leaves. As he struggled, one of his magic boots came off and remained stuck beneath the dead bird. He was very weak and with great difficulty staggered along till he reached the edge of the river; then Oni fainted again.

Early next morning the people came out to see the dead Anodo lying in the broken cotton tree. There was great rejoicing and drumming and the king soon appeared with his chiefs to view the wonderful sight. "Who is the great man who killed Anodo?" he asked. One of his hunters stepped forward and prostrating himself on the ground claimed that he was responsible for the deed.

"Then you will be rewarded generously, for I have promised to give half my kingdom to the man who killed Anodo and it is yours," replied the king.

There was great rejoicing and dancing and the hunter was carried to the king's palace and feasted. A very bedraggled figure then appeared; his clothes were torn and one of his boots was missing. It was Oni.

"Ah," said the king, "here is the stranger who calls himself Oni and who came yesterday to announce his intention of killing the eagle. You come too late, my friend, I fear."

"I killed Anodo. This man is an imposter and a liar," said Oni.

There was whispering between the king and his chiefs. At last he said, "Very well, you claim to have killed Anodo. What proof have you got to offer?"

"You see my condition," replied Oni, "but if you require further proof, send your men out to clear away the dead eagle and the broken cotton tree. Somewhere underneath you will find one of my boots."

The king ordered his men to go at once and search for the boot. After some little time the men returned. They carried Oni's magic boot. "We found it underneath the dead eagle's wing," they announced to the king.

"Now if you are still undecided and disbelieve my story, will you ask everybody to try on the boot and see if it fits," said Oni.

The king ordered everybody to try and see if they could fit the boot to their feet. Strange to relate, although it looked a perfectly normal boot, nobody could manage to put it on. When they had all tried without success, the boot was placed before the king and Oni stepped forward and said:

Boot from Heaven—boot from Heaven,
Go on to your master's foot.

Immediately, the boot started to move from before the king and fitted itself onto Oni's foot of

its own accord. The people and the king were convinced of the truth of Oni's claims and marveled greatly and were very delighted and grateful for his brave deed. The dishonest hunter was taken out and executed, and Oni received the promised reward.

That night, for the first time for many years, the bells of Ajo did not sound the curfew. Instead, the streets were full of happy, dancing people.

The Funeral of the Hyena's Mother

Today, all the wild animals in the world fear each other. This was not always the case, however, for long ago they used to like to meet together on ceremonial occasions for feasting and dancing, just in the same way as human beings do today. The change came suddenly and unexpectedly, and it was all due to the death of the hyena's mother.

In those far-off days, the animal world was divided up into many groups over which various animals ruled as chiefs, similar, in fact, to the way we are ruled in our country today. One such group was the Flesh-Eating Community, over which the hyena ruled. He was a most powerful ruler and thought a great deal of himself, and he was immensely proud of his family and of its great name and traditions.

Now Chief Hyena's father had died when Chief Hyena was very young, and so Mother Hyena had to train her son. This she had proceeded to do with great care and diligence. She taught him how to track and stalk and kill, to follow scents, and to conceal himself when danger was about. All this she taught him and much more besides. In fact everything that any young hyena should know was imparted to the young chief by his mother, until he was a very cunning animal indeed. So it was not surprising that Chief Hyena was very fond of his mother, and treated her with great respect when he grew up and became a full chief.

Then one day, when her time on earth was up, Mother Hyena died. Chief Hyena was much upset and he decided that his mother must have the finest burial that had ever been seen in the land. He called the animals together and told them that they must make preparations for a great funeral. There was to be great feasting and dancing after the burial ceremony, and it was to last many days. The details of the ceremony were arranged by the council and when they had been explained to the chief, he seemed pleased, and told them to make sure that all the important individuals from the various other animal groups were invited to take part in the ceremonies.

In actual fact, Chief Hyena was far from satisfied with his council's arrangements. He felt that something much more grand and spectacular was required for the last rites of such an important person as his late mother. So he called two of his particular old friends, the lion and the leopard, and suggested that they should round off the ceremonies by sacrificing ten of the animals from among the guests. By so doing they would have a good feast themselves, the gods would be appeased, and the spirit of Mother Hyena would have rest. The lion and the leopard thought that this was a most excellent suggestion. And so it was decided that during the singing and dancing on the way to the burial ground, the three of them should pounce simultaneously on the animals selected, and kill them.

The following day, the funeral of Mother Hyena took place. All the animals came and there was great singing and drumming as the procession made its way to the burial ground. None of the animals knew or suspected anything about the proposed ten sacrifices, and so, when Chief Hyena and his friends the lion and the leopard suddenly pounced on their victims there was great consternation amongst all the guests.

Chief Hyena killed a sheep, the lion killed a bird, and the leopard killed a goat. This caused much commotion and all the animals fled in terror, with the result that the other seven proposed victims were able to escape while the first killings were taking place.

When the three victims were dead, the killers found themselves alone with the body of Mother Hyena. Chief Hyena proposed that they should continue the ceremonies without the others, but lust for killing had been roused in the lion and leopard, and they told Chief Hyena to complete the ceremonies himself, while they went off to look for more victims to sacrifice.

From that day to this the animals have never again gathered together for social functions. The hyena family are disliked and feared by the other animals, and they live apart. The lion and leopard families are equally disliked and feared. They still roam the countryside, looking for victims to sacrifice for Mother Hyena, or so they say.

The peaceful and the bloodthirsty can never mix freely.

Taking a Sacrifice to Heaven

There was once a time when no rain fell upon the earth and the crops did not grow. The people accordingly arranged to offer a sacrifice to the gods to persuade them to send down the rain.

The people killed a ram and prepared everything for the sacrifice. Then they placed the carcass in a basket. All the birds had been summoned to attend the ceremony and one of them was chosen to fly with the sacrifice to Heaven.

But when the birds arrived they all refused to carry the sacrifice. Heaven was far off, it would mean a long and tiring journey for them, and they were far more interested in flying around and displaying their great beauty to each other. Work, even when it was connected with carrying a sacrifice to Heaven, was far too menial for any of them to undertake. They had never liked work.

The ega [1] thought his gold and black plumage

---

[1] ega—the village weaver bird.

the most beautiful of any, and he was far too restless and noisy to work for others, for, when he was not building nests, he was pulling down his old ones. The little red-billed ologiri [2] was far too busy hopping daintily about inside the houses and on the verandas and being very sociable to everybody. The olokoshe [1] was mating, and was very conspicuous because of his beautiful long tail and his magnificent black and white plumage. He was too occupied flitting after his wife to be troubled with sacrifices. And so it was with all the other birds: each one was unable to help for one reason or another, and each in turn refused.

[2] ologiri—red-billed fire finch.
[1] olokoshe—pin-tailed whydah.

At last the vulture, whom everybody despised, volunteered to carry the sacrifice. Everybody regarded him as a vulgar ne'er-do-well, who was ugly and spent all his time searching around the village rubbish dumps or following bush fires.

The vulture having agreed to carry the sacrifice, the people prepared a fire and, when this was ready, they heard him sing in his great voice:

> Oh what a war now exists,
> A serious war it is indeed,
> When the Earth and Heavens quarrel.
> The rain would not come down to Earth,
> And all the crops would not grow green.
>
> Heaven claims seniority
> Over Earth—Earth over Heaven.
> But no volunteers were found to take
> The sacrifice when it was ready.
> At last poor vulture came and did
> The arduous task all others refused.

Then he took the fire and the basket containing the ram's meat and departed for Heaven. Everybody watched him as his great wings carried him slowly away and he became a tiny speck high up in the blue sky.

Not long after he disappeared from sight, a great wind arose, and then the sky became dark

and heavy with rain clouds. Rain began to fall, to the accompaniment of great peals of thunder and flashes of lightning. So heavy were the rains that the dry, stony riverbeds soon became raging torrents and flooded the countryside.

When the vulture returned, he found the rains had destroyed his house. So he went to all the birds in turn, begging them to take him in, because he had helped them. But they were all too busy and selfish, and refused. Nobody wanted him and they drove him from their homes. The people also, like the birds, had forgotten his service and drove him away.

The vulture was now more bedraggled and ugly than ever. He was soaked with rain and the fire from the sacrifice had burnt the feathers from the top of his head and neck.

The vulture has remained an outcast among the birds from that day to this. He still loiters around the village markets and rubbish dumps or turns up at the bush fires, where he is not welcomed by the others. His burned feathers never grew again, a reminder to the selfish people who refused to help him.

Even the most despised are capable of doing good, and they are not always rewarded by their fellow men for their pains.

The Snail and the Leopard

Once in the Country of the Animals, there lived a leopard who had five children. This leopard was disliked very much by all the other animals because he was both crafty and dangerous.

A tortoise, who was the local barber to all the animals, called on the leopard one day and asked if he could cut the hair of the leopard's five children.

"Tortoise," roared the leopard, "it is an honor for you to cut the hair of my five fine children. You have my permission to cut their hair, but first of all you must cut mine. I will not pay, because of the honor you will derive from cutting our hair. See that you cut it well, or else you will suffer."

"I agree to cut it free. As you rightly say, O leopard, it is indeed an honor for me to cut the hair of the great leopard family. I would like to cut your hair up on the branches of that great tree over there," went on the tortoise. "All the other animals will be impressed when they see

69

you lying out on that branch having your beautiful hair cut."

"That is an excellent idea," replied the leopard. So he climbed up amongst the branches of the tree and lay out full length along a branch while the tortoise followed slowly behind.

The leopard yawned, flicked his tail, and then, closing his eyes, told the tortoise to proceed with his work and not take too long. The tortoise pretended to busy himself arranging the leopard's hair for cutting, but in actual fact he did nothing of the kind. One by one he took the leopard's hairs and tied them firmly to the branches of the tree till the leopard was securely bound. Then he pretended he had dropped his sharp knife and, excusing himself, he climbed down to pick it up.

When he had retrieved his knife he called the leopard's five children to come and watch their father's fine hair being cut. But when they came he caught and beat them all severely in front of their parent.

The leopard, on hearing their cries, gave a great roar of rage, which quickly turned to a cry of pain when he tried to jump down to punish the tortoise, for the tortoise had tied the leopard so securely that the animal was unable to move. In great fear the leopard's children ran away into the forest.

Soon all the other animals heard of the leopard's plight and came along in large numbers to laugh at him. Tied securely, the leopard begged them to come up and release him, but they all refused, knowing how crafty and dangerous he was. In this undignified position, the leopard remained tied up for two long days, while he was ridiculed by all the animals, and he became very hungry.

At the end of the second day, the leopard noticed a snail crawling along one of the branches of the tree, and he begged him to release him and promised to do anything the snail required in payment for his services.

The snail agreed to help the leopard, provided the leopard promised not to kill him after he

71

was released. To this the leopard readily agreed. So the snail set to work, and one by one, he untied the leopard's hairs from the branches.

When the leopard was free, he gave a great roar and sprang down from the tree. "Now my friend," he said to the snail, "I am going to teach everybody a lesson they will never forget. Never again will they be permitted to insult the leopard family, for I will kill to my heart's desire, and you are the first to die."

"You promised not to kill me," cried the snail, "if I released you."

"A leopard never makes a bargain," roared the leopard. "You have learned that lesson too late in your life, snail. Now I am coming up the tree and you will be the first to die."

The snail called out in a loud voice to the great God of the Sun, Oloja, to help him and save his life. The god heard his cry and sent an eclipse to obscure the sun, and so the earth was plunged into darkness and in that darkness the snail was able to make good his escape. Since that time, leopards have never had their hair cut by other animals. They never make bargains and have continued to roam the bush, looking out for every opportunity to revenge the insults they once suffered.

Why Tortoises Are Sacrificed

Once there was a very terrible famine throughout the land because there had been no rain. The ground had dried up and cracked and the crops had withered for lack of water. All the food was soon exhausted and people were dying in the streets from hunger.

The animals suffered too. Then one day the tortoise went out to look for food. As he traveled slowly along a small track that led to the town, he came across the stalk of an eggplant. It was green and fresh. "Somebody has food to drop. I wonder who he is, and where it comes from," thought the tortoise to himself. He saw the recent footprints of a man in the dry, powdery soil, so, being a wise tortoise, he followed them along. Eventually they led him to a house in the town. The tortoise then sat down patiently for the owner to come out. He waited there three long days; then, sure enough, a man came out carrying a hatchet. The tortoise could see that he was a farmer, and so he followed him quietly and unnoticed. The farmer and the tortoise walked a long way till at last they came to the banks of a great river. Nothing much remained of the river. It was only a tiny trickle between the huge rocks. The man continued along the riverbed for some distance until he came to a place where the river channel was close to the bank. Here a quantity of water had collected and on the bank the tortoise noticed the eggplants growing. Still unnoticed, the tortoise settled down to watch. The farmer watered and prepared his crops, and when he had completed his work and had collected some vegetables, he went home. The tortoise had made up his mind to make this place his home until the famine had passed.

Three days later, the farmer returned and was very angry when he noticed that somebody had been removing his eggplants. "Who has taken these things?" he shouted.

Now the tortoise was a musical tortoise, and during the three days he had spent at the farm, besides eating and sleeping, he had made himself a tiny flute from a piece of bamboo. When the farmer shouted, the tortoise, who was concealed in the roots of a big cotton tree, took his flute and started to blow and sing:

Who is the owner of the beautiful eggplant?
The beautiful vegetable so green and so fresh;
Who is he who will curse me for taking the food
While famine is in the land?

He is the farmer, the owner with sufficient;
The beautiful vegetable so green and so fresh,
Sufficient has he, but nothing over to spare
While famine is in the land.

The farmer was very surprised and frightened when he saw nobody about and a song coming, apparently, from a cotton tree. Instead of investigating, he took to his heels and never stopped running till he reached his home. The next day he reported the incident to his chief, and the chief prayed to Shango, god of thunder, to go to the cotton tree and destroy it with a thunderbolt. Shango heard and went to answer the chief's prayer. The tortoise could hear Shango coming across the dry riverbed. "Ah, here is the farmer coming back. I will sing again and drive him away," he said. So the tortoise picked up his flute and sang his song.

Shango was so surprised and frightened—for he knew none of his brother gods dwelled in the cotton tree—that he dropped his thunderbolt on the dry riverbed and took to his heels like the farmer.

When Shango told his brother gods, they refused to believe him. "No spirit dwells in that cotton tree," said Ogun, the god of iron. Ogun went to look, however. He crept up quietly to the cotton tree.

The tortoise, who was inside, did not hear him coming.

"As I thought, Shango was talking nonsense," said Ogun.

At that moment the farmer arrived.

"You see," said Ogun, "both Shango and you were wrong. No spirit dwells in that tree."

"The spirit talks only when I shout certain words," replied the farmer.

"What words?" asked Ogun.

"Who has taken these things?" said the farmer.

These words woke up the tortoise, who had been sleeping. "Ah," said the tortoise to himself, as he picked up his flute, "the farmer has returned," and he sang and blew on his flute, and Ogun and the farmer fled.

Many gods came to see and hear the cotton tree with the strange spirit. They would first call on the farmer and get him to show them the way, till at last the farmer got very tired of conducting the gods to his farm. People in the town were beginning to talk, and now knew

of his farm by the water. Besides, his eggplants were fast disappearing.

At last, Osanyin, the god of medicine, offered to go and investigate. He asked Ogun to lend him his blacksmith, who was called Ladi, and so Osanyin, Ladi, and the farmer set out for the farm. The farmer was very unwilling to go because the strange spirit had frightened so many of his gods, and he was now quite willing to sacrifice all his vegetables rather than remain near this strange juju.

When they reached the cotton tree, Osanyin made Ladi light a fire, and he placed a nail in the flames. The tortoise could see all these preparations from his hiding place and was so curious that he forgot to sing his song.

When the nail was red hot, Osanyin made the farmer call out, "Who has taken these things?"

"Ah, I have forgotten to sing my song and chase this foolish farmer and his friends away," thought the tortoise. So he picked up his flute and sang and blew his usual song.

"This is the last time I shall come here to witness this terrible juju," said the farmer, and he ran off. Osanyin and Ladi pretended to run too, only they hid in some nearby bushes and watched to see what would happen next.

The tortoise finished his song and laughed to

himself. "It is wonderful how my magic song drives all these people away! Now I will go and investigate this nail, and perhaps nibble some more of that delicious eggplant."

Osanyin and Ladi saw the "strange spirit" emerge from the roots of the cotton tree, and as the tortoise nibbled the eggplant, Ladi took the red-hot nail and nailed the tortoise to the ground. So perished the strange spirit of the cotton tree. Osanyin called the people to witness the cause of their fear, and then Osanyin said he would eat the tortoise.

Since that day tortoises have been sacrificed to the god of medicine, Osanyin.

Motinu and the Monkeys

In the Yoruba town of Owo, in ancient times, there dwelled a girl, Motinu by name. Motinu was of exceptional beauty and many offers of marriage were made to her by the young men of Owo, but for some reason best known to herself, Motinu refused them all.

Then one day, as she went to draw water from the nearby well, she saw a very handsome young man in magnificent clothes standing close to the water hole. Motinu was very surprised, not only because of his fine looks and rich clothes, but also because he was a complete stranger to her. She felt certain that he was not from Owo. As she stooped to fill her bowl, he spoke to her, "Motinu, would you like to come home and be my wife?"

"How do you know my name?" she asked.

"You are well known to me as the girl who refuses all offers made to you by the men of Owo. I am a stranger, and I have many possessions and friends. Although my people do not come from this town, yet they are powerful and influential. My home is not very far from here. Will you come along now and visit them and consent to be my wife?"

Motinu agreed to the young man's suggestion. She hurriedly returned home, packed a few of her belongings, and then followed the stranger.

She followed him out of the town and into the bush. He went on ahead at great speed and Motinu had difficulty in keeping up with him. After they had been traveling thus for a long time, Motinu, now breathless, stopped. "Where is your house?" she asked the young man.

"You just follow me," he replied, and went on as quickly as before.

At last, when Motinu had grown very tired,

the young man, who had now led her to a very thick and little frequented part of the bush, an area quite unknown to her, suddenly stopped and motioned her to sit down on a patch of open grass under some trees. "Wait there," he called to her. "I will go to my home and fetch my family."

Motinu was by this time rather frightened of the man, and was beginning to regret her rash decision to follow him. The young man had disappeared behind some thick bushes and was lost from sight. Something about his rapid movements and great agility frightened her still more. While she was thinking about all this, a large brown monkey suddenly appeared in the place where the young man had disappeared. With his long arms trailing on the ground, and using his knuckles, he came forward in a few quick bounds and sat down beside Motinu.

"I am your husband, Motinu," he suddenly said. "Here I live, and here you will live as my wife. You see I have great powers and can change myself into a man when I want to. Only I like to remain and live as a monkey here among my retainers and friends."

Motinu was now so frightened that she began to cry, but the monkey beat her with his horny black paws. She was certain that the monkey would kill her if she was not careful, and so she decided that the best thing to do would be to stop crying and agree to all the suggestions made by this strange animal.

The monkey now gave a jump and started chattering. Presently he was answered by similar noises, and before long many similar-looking monkeys appeared. Coming up to the grass patch, they all sat down quietly in a circle around Motinu. Some were busily engaged in minute personal inspection; others hung their heads on one side and pretended to look very wise; while others played with sticks in an aimless sort of way or examined each other. At last, when a large number of the creatures had gathered together, the talking monkey jumped up onto an overhanging branch and spoke to the others. Motinu could not understand what he said, but by the many gestures he made in her direction, she gathered he was talking about her. There was a great nodding of heads when at last he stopped chattering. Then turning suddenly to Motinu he said to her, "My family agree that you should stop here and become my wife. Pay great attention to what I have to say to you, and no harm will befall you. You must stay here in the bush and never return to man and his towns. We will give you a drum and you will drum every day for us while we dance. There will be little work for you to do, as we do not like our food cooked like man. Instead you will fetch water and wild fresh fruits for us."

So Motinu settled down to live with the monkeys. They gave her a wooden drum, and early in the mornings they would dance to the drum while she beat it. Then she was sent to draw water and fetch wild corn. After they had fed, the monkeys would all go off again to play by themselves in the bush, and so for about two hours every afternoon Motinu was able to lie down and rest. On their return, the monkeys would again make her drum for them while they danced. They did not hurt her, but she was very frightened of them, and did all she could to keep them amused and in good humor.

One day, as Motinu was gathering wild corn for the monkeys' meal, she was overjoyed to see a hunter passing close by, and she called softly to him. He was surprised to see a beautiful woman alone and so far from any town. She told him she was in great trouble and needed his help. Fearing that the monkeys would see him, she asked him to return in the afternoon when they would all be away.

Later, when she was alone, the hunter returned and Motinu told him her whole story.

She also told him that if he would only rescue her from the monkeys' clutches, she would gladly consent to become his wife. The hunter listened and promised to see what he could do. He told her to go on living with the monkeys as if nothing had happened until he came to her again.

On his return to Owo, the hunter called on a wood-carver in the town. He described to the carver Motinu's hair style and tribal markings, and asked him to make eight little images of her. When these had been carved and painted, the hunter carried them to the bush when he knew he would find Motinu alone. Then together, they set out quickly for Owo. Every few miles, the hunter dropped one of the carvings in a conspicuous place along the track. Ogunyemi, for that was his name, knew that these images would delay the monkeys when they tried to follow them. The hunter was correct. It was not long before they returned to dance, and found the wooden drum deserted and silent, and no Motinu. Furious, and chattering angrily, they set out in pursuit along the Owo track.

When the monkeys reached the first image, they were very curious indeed and sat down to chatter and argue.

"What is this," they said, "that bears such a

strong resemblance to Motinu?" They all tried to appear very wise, while they picked up the carving and turned it upside down and shook it. Then they rolled it about on the ground and played with it. None of them was wise enough to know what it was. At last, growing tired of it, they threw it away into the bush and went on in pursuit of their lost Motinu. There was more chattering and arguing when they reached the second image. Some declared that it was the same one that they had seen before, and that it had arrived in front of them by magic. To settle the matter, they returned to see if the first one was still where they had left it, and, satisfying themselves that it was, they set out in pursuit again. On reaching the third image there was more arguing and chattering. This time one of them seized the image and pulled off its arms and legs. Then they set off again. Each image they came to exasperated the monkeys more and more, and when they came upon one they would pounce on the image in anger and smash it up, chewing the pieces afterwards till nothing remained.

By this means Motinu and Ogunyemi were able to escape, but even so they were only just able to reach Owo in time, and as they entered the city they heard the loud chattering behind

86

them as the monkeys smashed up the eighth image. When they reached the mud walls of Owo, the monkeys were afraid to go any farther, but the one who had first appeared in the form of a man to Motinu now changed back into the same handsome young man as before and followed Motinu to Ogunyemi's house.

Motinu recognized him, however, and she told Ogunyemi who he was. The hunter reported the matter to the chief, with the result that the young man was caught and bound in chains. Because he could not return to the bush, he was unable to change back into a monkey, and he spent the rest of his days working as a slave for the chief.

As for Motinu and Ogunyemi, they were married and lived very happily together, and the monkeys never bothered them again.

The Twins

Once there lived in Yorubaland a man and his wife, and they had many children, but the children had all died very young, to the great grief of the parents. The wife begged her husband to consult an Ifa priest and ask him what the gods would require in exchange for sending him children who would live.

So the man went and told an Ifa priest his troubles, and the priest replied, "You must sacrifice all your goods and possessions. If you do this then the gods will give your wife two male children."

The man returned to his wife and told her the heavy sacrifice they would have to make in exchange for the children. "Then we must do it," replied the woman. "Even if it takes the last thing we have got," and so the woman prevailed on her husband and they sacrificed all their possessions.

They found the loss of their goods very great, but with the help of their relations they began to collect a home and goods together again. People, because of their faith, helped them. One person gave them a dog, while another presented them with a cat, and a third gave a hawk, and so on.

Then one day the husband went out early to fish and caught a very large and strange-looking fish. Dragging it to the bank, he cut the fish open and was surprised to find two knives and two swords inside the fish. He brought the fish, the knives and the swords back to show his wife, thinking it was a lucky omen, and found on his return that two sons had been born in his absence. They called them Taiwo and Kehinde. On the same day the cat also bore two kittens and the dog bore two puppies, while the hawk laid two eggs. The man's brother then went hunting in the forest, because it was customary in those days to give a present to a woman who had just had a child. He had not been hunting long before he killed a leopard which had just borne two cubs. "This is a lucky omen," said the man, and brought the dead leopard and her two live cubs as a present to the woman.

So they all grew up together and were very happy. Taiwo and Kehinde, as they grew, greatly resembled each other. They were very close friends and never quarreled.

When the twins had grown into young men,

they told their aging parents that the time had come for them to leave their home and to start to make their own way in the world. The father and mother were heartbroken and at first would not listen to their sons' suggestion. The father begged them to stay on and help with his farm. However, after further consultations, they yielded to Taiwo and Kehinde's desire to set out to seek their own fortunes. "There is little I can give you to take on your journey, my sons, but I will divide all the twins that came on the day you were born," said the father. So he divided them and gave to each twin a leopard, a hawk, a cat, a dog, a knife, and a sword.

Taiwo and Kehinde, together with the other twins, said good-bye to their father and mother, and then they all set out together. They walked for several days and passed several large towns. At last they came to a place where the road forked, and at the junction of the roads there was a great cotton tree.

Here the twins decided to separate, Taiwo taking the road to the left and Kehinde taking the one to the right. While they paused to say good-bye, Taiwo said to his brother, "Let us make a bargain, Kehinde, that we will meet in five years' time at this place."

"Right, we will all meet here five years from now," replied Kehinde. "Before we depart, let each of us take his knife and stick it into the cotton tree on the side that his road goes off. Then, if only one of us returns and looks at the other's knife and sees it is rusty and dull, he will know that the other is either dead, seriously ill, or in great trouble."

So the twins departed, each his own way. Kehinde, who took the right-hand road, traveled only a short distance, because he came to a town that attracted him very much, and he decided to settle down and make his home there. In this town, Kehinde studied medicine and became a native doctor of great skill.

As for Taiwo, he walked for many days until he reached the sea and then he followed the road along the coast until at last he came to a large town. He was surprised to find that all the women of the place had untied their hair. This in olden times was a sign of great distress, and he inquired of the people what their trouble might be.

"Alas, Olokun, the God of the Sea, has quarreled with the land over certain possessions, and when Olokun is vexed he tries to cover the land with water, and we have to appease and stop him by handing over the fairest maiden in the town each year. It has now come to the turn of the king's daughter to be sacrificed to Olokun, and for this reason we are in mourning."

"When is the sacrifice to take place?" inquired Taiwo.

"Today, when the sun is sinking in the west," a woman replied.

Taiwo said nothing, but later he inquired where the sacrifice was to take place and found that a deserted place on the seashore had been selected.

That evening, Taiwo went to the place and hid himself behind some trees and watched. The king's daughter was led down to the edge of the sea and bound to a stake, and after the ceremonies were over the people departed, leaving the girl to her fate.

When all was quiet, Taiwo went down and started to unbind the girl. She was very frightened and begged Taiwo to go away before the sea monster sent by Olokun came out of the water and drowned him too. She told him that nothing could now be done to save her, and the monster would certainly kill him too if he interfered. But Taiwo only laughed at her warnings and fears.

While Taiwo was unfastening the king's daughter from the stake, there came the noise of a great turmoil of water and a savage-looking sea monster with six heads came out of the sea. "Where is my prey for the year?" he shouted in a great voice with all his six mouths at once.

"Here I am," replied Taiwo calmly.

There then followed a bitter fight with the sea monster which lasted for two long days and nights. Taiwo was not alone in his struggle with the monster. While he attacked him with his sword, the leopard tore at the monster's body, the cat scratched his eyes, the dog bit the monster's legs, and the hawk flew down and pecked viciously. Even so, it was a bitter contest, and the monster would probably have won in the end if Taiwo had not called on the God of Thunder to help him. There then arose a great storm and the god sent down a thunderbolt, which killed the monster.

Taiwo then cut off the six heads with his sword. He next severed the ears from two of the heads, leaving the other four as they were. The ears he placed in a box along with his other possessions.

The king's daughter, who had stayed to witness the fight, was very grateful to Taiwo and she begged him to return to the king with her and tell him all that had happened and how the curse had been removed forever from the town and their people, but Taiwo only laughed and refused to go, saying that he must set out again on his travels. Before he went, however, the girl removed her necklace, and cutting it in two, she placed one half around the dog's neck and the other round the cat's neck as a token of her gratitude.

On her way back to her father, the king's daughter encountered one of her father's army generals. This man had promised the king to fight the sea monster, but at the last minute, before she was led away for sacrifice, he had made his excuses and departed. He was now very surprised to find her still alive and asked what had happened. The girl led him down to the shore and showed him the dead body and six severed heads of the monster lying on the shore, and explained how Taiwo and his animals, with the help of the Thunder God, had defeated Olokun's six-headed servant.

The general said nothing. He then led the girl back to her father, the king, and much to her surprise, he told her father how he had defeated and killed the monster himself with the help of the Thunder God. For proof, he sent his slaves down to the shore to bring back the six heads to the king, and it was not long before the people heard of the general's great deed and flocked down to see the monster's dead body. The king was delighted to have his daughter safe and to know there would be no further need to sacrifice to the sea monster. He announced to his people that he was going to marry his daughter to the general, and that when he died, having no sons, the general would become their king.

As for the princess, she hated the general for his lies, and told her father the story of Taiwo and his animals and how they had killed the monster. Nobody would believe her, however, thinking her fear had been so great at the time that it had turned her head and made her imagine these things.

The day of the marriage ceremony arrived, and there was great feasting and celebrating. Everybody was happy except the poor girl herself.

The day before the wedding was to take place, Taiwo chanced to return to the town. He found lodgings and then his dog wandered out into the market. It so happened that one of the slaves of the king's daughter happened to see it, and recognizing the necklace around the animal's neck as being part of her mistress's necklace, she ran back to the palace and reported what she had seen. The princess was delighted and told her to follow the animal till she found its owner and then come and tell her where he lived. The slave could not find the dog again in the crowded marketplace, but later as she wandered around, searching everywhere, she met Taiwo's cat and saw the other half of the princess's necklace. Following the cat, she was led to the house where Taiwo was staying; then she returned and told her mistress.

The princess ran to her father and told him the whole story again concerning the killing of the six-headed monster by Taiwo and his animals. This time she did not forget to relate how she had placed her necklace around the necks of the cat and the dog, and how her slave had found and followed the animals, and had at last discovered where Taiwo was living.

"Before the wedding takes place, this matter must be cleared up," said the king, and he ordered his attendants to follow the slave to the house and to bring Taiwo and his animals before him. The king also sent for the general.

When they had all arrived, the king ordered them to state their cases. The general spoke first. He related how he had gone down to the shore after the ceremonies were over and released the princess. How he had fought and killed the monster with the help of the Thunder God, and had then cut off his heads, and for proof the general had the six heads brought to the palace and placed before the king.

Then the king turned to Taiwo and asked him to state his case. Taiwo related the story of the killing and when he had finished he asked those assembled to look closely at the monster's heads and to tell him what was peculiar about them.

The king and his attendants examined the heads carefully, and they soon discovered only four of the six heads had ears. The other two were without.

"Why is this?" the king asked the general.

"So the monster was when he first came out of the water. Only four of the heads had ears, but is it of any importance? I have produced the six heads, what more proof do you require? And what better proof has this upstart got to offer us while he interferes with the marriage ceremonies?" demanded the general in an angry voice.

"Only this," said Taiwo, and as he spoke he opened a packet he carried with him and held up the four severed ears from the two heads of the monster. "If you look closely at these four ears you will see that they resemble closely the ears on the other four heads, and they belong to the two heads without any ears," Taiwo continued. The two sections of the princess's necklace were next taken from the dog and cat and rejoined, and the princess replaced them around her neck that all might recognize it as belonging to her.

The king and his counselors were now satisfied with Taiwo and the princess's story. They found the general guilty and ordered him to be taken out of the palace and his ears and head to be cut off as a punishment for his lies. The marriage ceremonies were continued and the princess was married to Taiwo. Taiwo, the princess, the leopard, the cat, the dog, and the hawk, and the sword all lived together in the palace with the king. The necklace was again broken and presented to the cat and the dog by the princess in gratitude for their help in finding Taiwo, and for saving her from the general.

Two seasons later, the old king died and the people of the town gathered together and elected Taiwo as their new king, for he was greatly respected and admired by everybody for what he had done. Taiwo ruled peacefully for three years.

As he sat in the palace one day, he thought that the time was approaching for him to return to the cotton tree at the road junction, and to meet his brother again as they had arranged. He wondered how his brother was, and what he and the other twins had been doing, and if they had served his brother as well as his had served him. While Taiwo sat thinking about the coming meeting and working out the number of days that remained before he would again meet Kehinde, he heard a great commotion in the palace. His wife came and told him that a large cock had entered the royal compound and was making a fearful noise, and that none of their servants or slaves could drive it out. Taiwo went out into the compound and tried to drive the cock away, but it would not go for him either. When he tried to shoot it with his arrows they all missed. It continued to crow at him in a great voice. It was the largest cock Taiwo had ever seen in his life. At last he gave up trying to kill the cock and returned to his apartments. The cock followed, and perching on one of the windows it continued to crow at him.

At last, greatly annoyed, Taiwo sent for the leopard, the cat, the dog, and the hawk; and taking his sword he chased the cock out of his palace. This time the cock did not stop, he fled before the twins, out of the town, and then down towards the sea where Taiwo had killed the sea monster five years before. Here Taiwo expected something strange to happen, for he realized the bird was no ordinary cock, but the cock led the twins on for many miles along the shore, and although they all traveled very fast in pursuit, none of them was able to catch up with it.

It was nearly sundown when the cock, turning suddenly from the shore, darted into the woods that fringed the coast.

At this point Taiwo noticed a small farm, and when they reached it, he decided to investigate a compound at the back of the farm, as it was very probable the cock came from there. When the twins entered the compound, they found it deserted. The cock was not to be found anywhere. After searching for a long time, they were on the point of departing when a very old woman appeared and asked them what they were looking for.

"I am looking, Mother, for a large cock that came to my town and annoyed us. I have chased him for most of the day, and he has led us to this place. Now I am unable to find him. Do you know this cock or have you ever seen him?" asked Taiwo.

"Indeed I know him only too well, I fear. He has pestered me for many years and has driven my husband into the sea. If only you would kill him I should be more than grateful to you. Stay a little while and he will return, for he is hiding in the woods and will come here when he thinks you have gone," replied the old woman. "You must all be very tired after your long chase. I only wish you had killed him before he came back here. Now sit down here and rest, and I will give you some palm wine to refresh yourselves."

So Taiwo and his animals sat down and rested, for they were tired after their long chase. The old woman fetched some palm wine and they all drank. Then she left them to rest.

After a little while the old woman returned. Taiwo noticed a great change in her face. She was now grinning at them, and behind her strutted the cock.

"King Taiwo, you and all your animals are in a trap. You have been brought here by my servant, the cock. This is the house of the sea monster you murdered five years ago, and I am his mother. I have long waited patiently to catch you, and now at last you have come and you will die here," the old woman cackled.

With a cry, Taiwo sprang up, and raising his sword, he was about to strike the old woman when he noticed all the twins had turned into stone images as they prepared to spring at the old woman. "The magic palm wine is working, you see," screamed the old woman. Then Taiwo's upraised arm holding the sword turned to stone and he was unable to move. Slowly he felt the life in his body departing, and a short while afterwards the old woman and the cock were left with six stone images. "Six stone images for the six severed heads of my son," said the old woman to the cock, with a terrible laugh, and the cock crowed.

When at last the period of five years had elapsed, Kehinde, who had all this time been practicing medicine in the town near the road junction, packed up his medicines and set out to find his brother Taiwo. With him went his leopard, cat, dog, hawk, and sword.

When they reached the cotton tree, Kehinde went and looked at his brother's knife. It was still stuck into the tree but it was very rusty, while the blade of his knife, on the opposite side of the tree, shone brightly. "Taiwo will not be meeting us here today. Some mishap has befallen our twins," said Kehinde to the others.

None of them had any idea where Taiwo had gone, and they therefore decided that the only thing to do was to set off along the road Taiwo's party had taken five years before, and search for the twins.

They walked for many days until they reached the sea. There they followed the road along the coast until at last they came to Taiwo's town.

Taiwo had now been missing for nearly a month and his wife and the people of the town were very worried. Messengers had been sent out to search the countryside for the missing king and his strange followers.

As Kehinde approached the town accompanied by his leopard, cat, dog, hawk, and sword, he was seen by the searching messengers and it was not surprising that they immediately mistook Kehinde for the missing Taiwo, so alike were all the twins. They rushed back to tell the town the good news of Taiwo's return.

When Kehinde reached the town, he was very surprised to hear the royal drum being sounded, and still more surprised when the townspeople came out and greeted him as their missing king. All pressed around him asking him many questions about where he had been and why he had stayed away so long. "This is undoubtedly my brother's town and he seems to have done well for himself since he left me five years ago at the cotton tree. Only I wonder where he went to—these people do not know," thought Kehinde to himself.

While Kehinde was standing in the market-place, surrounded by the happy townspeople and considering what he should do next, a large cock suddenly appeared in front of him as if from nowhere, and started to crow in a loud voice. There were angry cries from the townspeople when they saw the cock. They tried to drive it away from Kehinde, but the cock refused to go. Some threw sticks and stones at the bird, but they never managed to hit it. Kehinde was rather amused and wondered why a large cock should annoy the townspeople so much. When Kehinde moved towards the cock, he noticed it moved quickly away. "That is the

103

same cock you chased out of the town one month ago. Now it has come back with you. Where have you been with him all this time?" some of the old counselors asked Kehinde.

Kehinde listened carefully to the old men's questions. Obviously the cock had been responsible for his brother's disappearance. Calling to his leopard, cat, dog, and hawk to follow him, he set out in pursuit of the large cock, while the people begged him to stay, and to return to his wife in the palace, and not to follow the evil bird again. "This must be a magic bird," said Kehinde when he saw that the animals and the hawk were unable to catch it. He gave up chasing it and followed it at a walking pace. The cock would stop and let them almost reach him before he moved forward again. In this way they followed the cock all day along the seashore until they came to the farm of the old woman who owned the cock. Kehinde had long since ordered the people to return to the town and await him there. He had not told them who he was, or that his twin brother Taiwo was their king, and still missing.

It was sundown when Kehinde reached the old woman's farm, and she was standing in the doorway waiting for him.

"Greetings," she said when he reached the door.

"Do you own that large cock?" asked Kehinde.

"Yes," replied the woman, "I sent the cock to bring you here from your brother's town, for I think I know what you are seeking for. Is it not King Taiwo, his leopard, cat, dog, hawk, and sword?" continued the old woman.

"Yes, that is correct," replied Kehinde, "but how do you know all this?"

"I want to help you find your twin brother and the twins of your animals and bird. You see, they passed this way one month ago and I begged them to stay and rest here for the night, but they would not. Now I fear they have encountered some difficulties and perhaps dangers, but if you come in and rest a little while, I will give you all some palm wine to drink while I tell you how you can see your brother again."

So Kehinde and his followers entered the old woman's house and sat down, while she fetched a large bowl of palm wine.

Kehinde had practiced medicine for a long time, and he knew he must be on his guard against this old woman and her palm wine. When Kehinde had refreshed himself, the old woman passed the wine to the animals and the hawk and they all drank to satisfaction.

"Have you all drunk from the bowl?" the old woman asked.

"We all have," replied Kehinde.

"Good, now if you will all come with me I
will lead you to the place where you can see
your brothers."

She lit an oil lamp and led them out of the
house into a large walled compound at the back.
"In that hut over there you will find them. Go
and look." Kehinde, followed by the others, went
and looked. Standing in a row under a thatched
roof they saw their twins all motionless and as
if made of stone.

The old woman came forward, holding her
lamp up so that they might have a better view,
"You see, they too drank of my palm wine and
now I have fulfilled my promise to show you
your brother. You will all remain united and in
two rows facing each other."

"Can nothing bring them back to life?" asked
Kehinde in a frightened voice.

The old woman laughed. "Look," she said,
pointing at Kehinde's hawk and animals. "They
are already turning to stone, and in a few
seconds you will be like them with the blood
in your body cold and congealed. However, I
will tell you before you die," she went on, as she
noticed Kehinde standing rigidly, "in my house
stand two large calabashes of magic liquid. If
these were poured over you, you would all be
restored to life, but only I know this, and I
intend to leave you as images forever in my

compound as a punishment for killing my son, the sea monster with six heads. It is now too late for you to escape," she added with an evil laugh.

"It is a pity for your sake that I studied medicine," retorted Kehinde, moving forward from his pretended still pose. The old woman uttered a cry and backed towards the house. "Before you gave me the bowl of palm wine to drink, I took some of my medicine from this leather pocket you see here, and your spells have no power to harm me."

The old woman tried to run away, but Kehinde was too quick for her and with one blow of his sword, he had killed her.

Running into the house, he searched for the two calabashes of magic fluid. He found them hidden away in a dark corner and returned quickly to the compound and splashed some of the liquid over his brother Taiwo and all the twins. Life was immediately restored to all of them.

There was great rejoicing that night. It was the first time they had met for five years, and everyone was able to explain what had befallen them since they parted at the cotton tree. Once again all the twins were united and happy. They burned the old woman's house, and finding the cock, they slew him too, and threw the old woman and the cock into the fire. The next morning they departed for Taiwo's town, taking with them the two calabashes of magic liquid.

"We are all as much alike as ever," said Taiwo, when Kehinde related how the townspeople had mistaken him for his brother. "When we return to the town let us each enter by different gates. You go around by the south gate, and I will enter by the north gate. When we reach the palace it will be amusing to see if my wife recognizes which of us is her husband."

Before they reached the town they separated into two parties, as arranged. The chief in the south section of the town saw Kehinde with his leopard, cat, dog, hawk, and sword coming, and thinking he was Taiwo, he sent a slave running to order the sounding of the royal drum that stood outside the palace in the center of the town.

Taiwo arrived at the north gate with his party at the same time as his brother reached the south gate, and the chief at the north gate, on being told the king was approaching, sent a runner to sound the drum too. There was great confusion at the palace and nobody knew where to post the guards. Taiwo's wife, hearing the noise, came out of the palace to see what was happening. The sound of cheering townspeople came towards the palace from two directions, and when both parties met there was general surprise at finding two kings, two leopards, two cats, two dogs, two hawks, each twin exactly like the other. Taiwo's wife was as confused as the townspeople, and did not recognize which of the twins was her husband. They laughingly called on her to point out which of them was her husband. At first she was confused, and then, remembering something that had helped her before, she asked both parties to separate. They stood apart looking exactly alike in appearance, but there was one little difference the brothers had overlooked: around the necks of one dog and one cat hung the royal necklace. And so she was able to recognize her husband.

So Taiwo ruled as king, and his brother Kehinde and all the other twins lived together in the palace with him.

At the end of two seasons, Kehinde suggested to Taiwo that they should go home and see their parents. It was now seven long years since the twins had left their home. Taiwo agreed, and a few days later they all set out. When they passed the cotton tree, they found their two knives still stuck in the tree as they had left them, the only difference being that this time Taiwo's was no longer rusty. It shone as brightly as Kehinde's. "Because we are returning to our parents, there is no need to leave the knives in the cotton tree," said Taiwo. So the two brothers removed their knives from the tree and set out for home.

Taiwo and Kehinde, on reaching their parents' home, were grieved to find it empty and in ruins. The grass roof had fallen in and the mud walls were crumbling. There was no sign of their father or mother. On inquiring from some people who dwelled near by, they learned that their mother had died a few years before. Their father had been drowned shortly afterwards while he was fishing in a river.

Taiwo and Kehinde inquired of their mother's grave, and going to the spot, Kehinde unfastened his loads. "I have brought along with me the magic liquid we found in the old woman's house, that which I poured over you to bring you back to life. Let us pour it over our mother's grave and see what happens," he said to Taiwo. Taiwo agreed, and they poured the liquid from one calabash over the grave. Immediately there was a great rumbling and the ground began to move under their feet. Kehinde hurriedly gave the second calabash to his hawk to carry away and the twins moved quickly from the spot as the ground rose. Soon the ground was split asunder and over the spot where their mother's grave had been, there appeared a great rock— Olumo. The rock can be seen at Abeokuta to this day.

After the brothers had witnessed this strange happening, they inquired of the place where their father had been drowned and going there, they took the magic fluid from the second calabash, which the hawk had carried, and poured it on the water. Gradually the waters from the river spread out until it formed what is now the Osa Lagoon at Lagos. In this way the twins erected two great memorials to their parents.

Taiwo and Kehinde returned to the town where Taiwo reigned as king, and after a very

long stay with his brother, Kehinde decided to return to his home and practice medicine as before. Taiwo wanted him to stay on with him, but he would not, and so the twins were at last parted, and Taiwo and his twins accompanied him to the cotton tree.

Not long after his return, Kehinde died, and with him died his leopard, cat, dog, and hawk. Kehinde and his animals and bird were taken up to Heaven, and people still say that he appears as the moon in the sky at nights. As for Taiwo, he reigned as king for a very long time, and had many children. When at last he died, his leopard, cat, dog, and hawk died too. His son succeeded him, and became the first king of Oyo.

The Hen and the Hawk

There once lived a hen who was very worried because when she took her chickens out into the bush to search for food, they were always attacked by either snakes or foxes. However much the hen kept a sharp lookout for her enemies they always succeeded in devouring some of her children.

One day, growing tired at last of this perpetual anxiety, she decided to go and speak to a certain hawk who was reputed to be very wise and seemed to know a lot about powerful jujus.

When the hen had cackled at great length to the hawk and had asked for his help, the hawk replied that he was quite willing to assist the hen with one of his jujus, but in return for it, she would be obliged to hand over two out of every ten chickens. The hen readily agreed to the bargain, thinking to herself that it was far better to lose two out of every ten than run the risk of losing them all.

So the hawk prepared the juju and gave it to the hen.

Not long afterwards, the hen produced a brood of twenty chickens and she was delighted to find that wherever she went with them, neither the snakes nor the foxes attacked them, and they all lived in peace. So it continued with her second and third brood; they all lived like the first, and all seemed immune from attack.

The hen now had sixty chickens and was immensely proud of her family. One thing, however, the hen did not do: she failed to keep her part of the bargain with the hawk concerning the handing over of two out of every ten chickens.

In due course the hawk learned of the hen's large family, and remembering his bargain, he flew down to see the hen and claim his share.

The hen was very indignant indeed and had a lot to say and refused to hand over twelve of her children to the hawk. This not unnaturally made the hawk very angry, so away he flew and reported the matter to one of the gods, Orisha by name. Orisha gave him permission to take any he could lay his talons on, up to the number of twelve. Being unable to carry twelve chickens away at one time, the hawk swooped down on the hen and removed them one by one, and so, up to today, the hawk has continued to come and remove the chickens one by one.

Nonfulfillment of a promise is a dangerous thing.

Concerning the Egas
and Their Young

The ega is the beautiful little black and ·yellow bird which is found all the way from Senegal to the Cameroons. It lives in the northern thorn shrub and grass woodland belts, and in clearings in the equatorial forests. It lays two eggs, which vary from white to sky blue and purple. When it is not building a nest, it will be pulling down its old one. It is a restless and noisy bird and both a bold and aggressive fighter, but when its nests are raided by large hawks, which quite frequently happens, and the young nestlings are taken, the ega makes no noticeable protest.

How this all came about is an interesting story. A very long time ago, and just before the incident when the vulture had had his feathers burned taking the sacrifice to heaven, there lived an ega and his wife. The wife had laid two of the most beautiful eggs that the ega had ever seen; one was sky blue and the other a shade of purple. The ega was immensely proud of these

and called all the other birds to come and see
them. The beauty of their home, which was built
of strips of palm fronds and grass, seemed to
be completed by these two beautiful eggs. The
nest became the talk of the countryside.

The ega was more noisy and restless than ever
and seemed never to be still. His shrill clamorous
chirping began to annoy the other birds, who
regarded him as very conceited and they wished
him, his wife, the two beautiful eggs, and their
nest the worst of fortune. Strange to relate,
these ill wishes came true and the good luck of
the ega family seemed to change, for when the
two eggs were hatched out they turned out to
be two very objectionable and disobedient young

nestlings. They would do nothing their parents asked them, and when they were ordered to leave the nest so that it could be cleaned they flatly refused to move out. As the young ones grew, they became more and more lazy, leaving their parents to fetch them fruits and seeds from the shrubs, and rice and corn from the farms. Nothing would persuade them to leave the nest, and it became very dirty indeed. The parents did all they could to improve the young egas, but without success. At last they decided to move away from their once beautiful home and build another, telling their children that they must stay on in the old nest and in future fend for themselves.

With great patience and diligence the new ega home was built, and no sooner was it completed than the young ones flew out of the old nest and came to live in the new one with their parents. There was no improvement in their manners, however, and the same thing happened again. Furious, the father ega said he would not tolerate the position any longer, and he set to work; and blade by blade and leaf by leaf he pulled down his new home till nothing remained of it.

When the young ones had thus been forced out, they at once flew off and reported the whole matter to the king of the birds, the eagle. They said that they had been driven out by their parents to fend for themselves.

The eagle called the parents and the young ones together to settle the matter. The father eagle said he would not allow the young ones to live with him any longer. However, the eagle said that as the parent he was responsible for looking after the young, and found him guilty. As a punishment he was ordered by the eagle to go on building nests for ever.

That is why egas are everlastingly pulling down or rebuilding their nests, and perhaps that is the reason why they are not greatly perturbed when hawks raid their nests and seize their young.

The Elephant and the Cock

In the Country of the Animals, there once arose
a dispute between the elephant and the cock.
The elephant had for long been proclaimed as
the strongest animal, and he had for a long time
accepted this as a fact. It therefore came as a
great surprise to him one day when, at a meeting of all the animals, the cock suddenly jumped
up and contradicted the elephant. "No, my
friend," he crowed, "you think that on account
of your huge ungainly size that you have the
right to assume the role of 'strongest of all creatures.' You are a clumsy, ungainly animal who
does not know how to use what strength the
gods have given you."

"If I am not the strongest of all animals," replied the elephant, "then perhaps you would be
good enough to tell me who is. I shall be interested to learn of a greater animal than myself, because I have yet to meet him."

"I am not talking about the size of animals,"

replied the cock, "I am talking about their strength and powers. What is size without power?"

"What is size without power?" answered the elephant. "You speak the truth, my friend, but you have still to tell me who is the strongest of all creatures."

"I am," crowed the cock. At this there was great excitement amongst all the animals. Some were amused and some were annoyed with the cock and his loud bragging ways. The elephant remained unmoved, and when the excitement had died away he slowly arose, and flicking his great trunk majestically he said, "O cock, look well upon me, for here you see the king of the

jungle, the strongest and largest of all the animals of the kingdom. Wherever I walk I leave behind me roads that all may witness my passing. Nothing remains in my way. I smash tracks through the thickest forest and even the great, fully grown palm trees can be uprooted by the twist and power of my trunk. What other animal can do such things?" roared the elephant. "Let him speak now if he wishes."

There was great applause for the elephant when he sat down again.

Then the cock stood up. "What is your great and clumsy strength fit for? All other animals move quietly and quickly through the forest, leaving no marks of their passing; they pass silently on their way and in stalking their prey. What use is your stupid tree-smashing? I am the strongest of all living creatures, for I can wake people up from the deepest of sleep. I can perform many wonders, even to the awakening of the dead if I so desire. I am the god that summons the sun back to the earth, with my great voice, the guard and summoner of light," replied the cock.

After this speech there was a silence amongst the animals. At last the tortoise spoke, "Let there be a contest fixed between these two and we can then judge who is the strongest creature on earth."

The idea met with the general approval of the company. The elephant and the cock were equally agreeable to the tortoise's suggestion, and the contest was fixed to take place in a few days' time.

On the appointed day all the animals assembled in the forest for the trial of strength between the two. First came the turn of the elephant. A large and dense track of forest had been selected by the Animals' Council, and with a great bellow the elephant charged down on the spot. Soon clouds of earth and laterite were rising in the air, and the elephant was completely hidden from the onlookers. Trees, branches, and stones rose high above the dust clouds, and there was a terrible noise of splintering wood.

Now it so happened that the Animals' Council had selected a section of the forest that was infested with thousands and thousands of tiny insects. And as the elephant smashed his way through the forest, these insects, in great fear of their lives, hurriedly settled on his body, it being the securest place of refuge. So as the elephant went on, his body became covered with thousands upon thousands of insects, until they completely weighed him down with their great numbers. In his great fury and concentration on the contest, and because of the clouds of dust

123

that arose on all sides of him, he did not see them, but he felt his body growing heavier and heavier. At last, tired out and exhausted and weighed down by his great weight, the elephant gave up smashing this track through the forest; and throwing himself down on the ground, he was soon fast asleep.

The cock had been watching the elephant all this while, and when at last he saw his rival fall asleep, he came up and perched on his body and began to peck the insects off one by one and devour them. He did not eat them all, however, for directly the insects found the elephant had fallen, they made haste to return to their smashed and broken homes to inspect the damage caused by the great animal. While the elephant slept on, the cock went on pecking, slowly picking off and eating what insects remained, until at last the elephant's body was completely cleared of them. In fact, the elephant had never been so free of insects in his life before.

At long last, he awoke to find himself surrounded by laughing and jeering animals, and his track unfinished. Perched on his back stood the cock, and the elephant felt him pecking at his back. He got up quickly and as he did so, he was amazed to find his body so very light. The elephant did not stop to inspect further, for a great fear had seized him because he could feel the pecks of the cock all over his body, and his lightness at once led him to believe that he was being slowly eaten away by the cock.

With a great bellow of fear he smashed his way into the forest, shouting that he had no wish to remain and be eaten by a cock, and that in future he would not participate in any more contests that were not fairly conducted. Thus ended the trial of strength between the elephant and the cock.

Since that day, the elephant has kept himself to the depths of the forest and bush, and far from the sound of crowing cocks. As for the cock, he was not proclaimed by the Animals' Council to be "the strongest creature on earth," but his conceit never left him, and ever since that time all cocks have looked upon themselves as creatures of great importance and power.

The Hunter and the Hind

Many years ago there lived a hunter called Ogunlola. Every day he went with his bow and arrows to hunt in the bush. Ogunlola was the finest hunter in his village. He was popular because he seldom returned empty-handed, and everyone had plenty of meat. In exchange for the game he killed, the people used to supply him with yams, plantains, rice, and palm wine.

One day Ogunlola wandered farther into the bush than usual, and he came to a district he did not know. It was his custom, when hunting, to climb trees and wait there quietly for the animals. So he looked round and selected a large iroko tree. He climbed up and hid himself. He waited patiently for a very long time, but no game passed his way all day and he grew tired. Night was now not far off, and as he had a long way to go before reaching his home, he began to climb down the tree. Then, suddenly, he saw a hind standing perfectly still under a bush, only a few paces away.

Raising his bow, Ogunlola was about to take aim, when to his amazement the hind began to remove its skin and become a very beautiful woman. In fact, she was one of the most beautiful women Ogunlola had ever seen. When the transformation was complete, the woman placed the hind's skin under a stone lying close to Ogunlola's tree. Then she slipped away silently into the twilight and was lost from sight.

Ogunlola was very surprised at what he had just seen and waited some time in the hope that the woman would return. But when there was no sign of her he climbed down, picked up the skin, and went home with it.

The next morning before daybreak, Ogunlola got up, and taking the skin of the hind, he placed it in a cotton bag that one of his wives had woven. Slinging the bag over his shoulder, he set out once again for the iroko tree in which he had hidden on the previous day.

Again Ogunlola waited all day. No game passed by and the beautiful woman did not reappear. He did not put the skin back under the stone, but kept it with him in the tree. Then when night was approaching, and it was time to return home, the woman suddenly reappeared.

Going to the stone she began to search for the skin. Ogunlola watched her for a little while and then called out to ask what she was seeking. The woman was startled, but her anxiety to find the hind's skin drove away her surprise and fear of the hunter. She answered that she was looking for a hind's skin that had been hidden under the stone. She suspected the hunter knew where the skin could be found and she promised that she would give him a present if he helped her to find the skin.

As she was very beautiful, Ogunlola told her all he had seen on the previous evening and said that he would give her the skin if she promised to return to his house and marry him. Ayinke, for that was the woman's name, said she would, on condition that Ogunlola promised never to reveal the secret of the transformation to any living creature. This he gladly agreed to do. So Ayinke gave him the hind's skin as the present she had promised, and they set out for the hunter's home.

Now the hunter had two other wives, and they were very surprised when Ayinke appeared, for she was not from their village, and they had never seen her before. Ogunlola explained that he had met her at a distant village on one of his hunting expeditions. Everybody in the village accepted the hunter's explanation, and the two wives, who were called Abake and Ashake,

128

gladly welcomed her to their home, for she was gentle as well as beautiful. So Ogunlola and Ayinke were married. There was great feasting and dancing in the village, and it was many days before Ogunlola returned to hunt in the bush. Ogunlola, Ayinke, Abake, and Ashake all lived very happily together, and presently, a fine son was born to Ayinke. They called him Ogunrinde.

The hunter had kept the skin of the hind ever since his marriage to Ayinke. Several times he had considered destroying it, but he decided not to, fearing the magic of the skin and the consequences of such an act. In the meantime, Ayinke was happy and very fond of her child.

Towards the close of the second year of their marriage however, just before the rains were due to begin, a change gradually came over Ayinke. It was very gradual at first, but she seemed no longer content with her life in Ogunlola's house. She grew restless and discontented, and even began to lose interest in Ogunrinde, her son.

Ogunlola noticed the change. Although he said nothing, he felt that his young wife was longing to return to the wild life of the bush. So one day when Abake and Ashake had gone to the market and Ayinke had gone to draw water, he took the skin of the hind and hid it among the kola nuts he kept in baskets hung from the roof of his house.

One day, not very long after this, Ayinke asked her husband for the skin, but he refused to tell her where he had hidden it. She repeated her request many times, but Ogunlola always refused to tell her. By the end of the rains the relationship between Ogunlola and Ayinke had grown very strained, and every day now she demanded that the skin be returned to her. Up to this time they had both been very careful never to mention the subject in front of Abake and Ashake, but as time passed and their anger grew, they became careless, with the result that the other wives knew the cause of the trouble between their husband and Ayinke.

Every day, when Ogunlola had departed for the bush, Ayinke searched for the skin, and though Abake and Ashake would often ask her what she was looking for, she refused to tell them. Then one day they pretended that they were going to the market, but instead, they hid themselves behind some grass mats in the compound and watched Ayinke as she continued her search. They saw her take a ladder and climb up into the rafters, where she discovered the hind's skin hidden amongst the kolas. Then to their amazement they saw her put on the skin and change into a hind. Having done so, she fled from Ogunlola's house.

Abake and Ashake were very angry with Ogunlola. They both said he had taken an animal to wife and brought it to live among their people. They hurried at once to their families and told them the story, and the matter was soon reported to their chief, who summoned a meeting.

In the meantime, the hind had found her husband Ogunlola while he was hunting in the bush. She came bounding towards him, and before he had time to shoot, she started to sing:

> O my husband the hunter,
> Please do not shoot at me,
> I put on my silver coat
> While you were away,
> I have shared my belongings
> And given them to my son,
> Please do not shoot me,
> My husband Ogunlola.

Then she told him that because of his obstinate refusal to give her the skin, she now had no wish to return to live with him as his wife. Henceforth she would remain a hind, and he could go his own way and make what explanations he liked to his other wives and their relations about her disappearance.

131

Stupefied, Ogunlola watched her as she fled into the bush. When he returned to the village, bewildered and greatly upset, he found the people had turned against him. He was taken before the chief and charged with taking an animal to wife and of bringing it to live in the village. The chief was very angry and ordered Ogunlola and his son Ogunrinde to be banished to the bush. They must never again enter the village, or they would be killed.

So Ogunlola and Ogunrinde went to live in the bush, alone and uncared for. Ogunlola had lost everything: his good name, all his wives and property; only his bow and Ogunrinde remained. He lived a long time and kept himself and Ogunrinde by hunting, but as the boy grew up he became very wild, and preferred to live like the wild animals. Then one day he too disappeared.

Ogunlola lived on by himself and though he lived to be an old man, he never saw either Ayinke or Ogunrinde again. Finally, when he died, he was completely alone and uncared for.

Be content with what you possess, for by seeking what is strange you may end by losing all.

Oniyeye and
King Olu Dotun's Daughter

A very long time ago, and soon after our forefathers had come to Yorubaland, there lived a
king called Olu Dotun. This king had only one
child, a very beautiful daughter, and when she
reached a marriageable age, her father was unable to decide to whom she should be married.
Many young men had asked for the girl as wife,
but the king had refused them all. In order to
rid himself of the many suitors that called at his
palace, he announced one day, half in jest, that
any man in the kingdom who was able to produce an animal with one hundred and fifty-two
tails could have half the kingdom and the hand
of his daughter in marriage.

The king's news was received with great surprise by all the hunters. One of them, called
Oniyeye, who was reputed to be the finest of
them all in the king's dominion, made up his
mind that if such an animal existed in the world,
he would hunt it down and bring it to the king.

First he went and called on an Ifa priest and

asked him to find out if there really was such an animal in the world. The priest, for a small gift, promised to consult his jujus and let him know. Three days later the Ifa priest called him back. "Yes," said the old man, "such an animal does exist today, but only one remains in the whole world. My juju tells me that it dwells in a far-distant hollow mountain, but where it is I do not know. Nobody can reach it except in his dreams, and if you do ever happen to dream of the animal you must make a sacrifice to the gods on waking. Beyond this I can tell you nothing more, my son."

Oniyeye thanked the old Ifa priest and departed.

For a long time the hunter tried to find out

how he could reach the hollow mountain where the animal with a hundred and fifty-two tails dwelled. At last he thought of a plan.

He told all his friends and brother hunters that he was going away on a long journey and would not be returning for two months, and so he set out with his bow and arrows, and armed with his hunter's talisman.

Setting off for the forest on foot, he traveled for several days, until he came to a district where many of the wild animals congregated.

Oniyeye searched about until he discovered an open glade. This showed signs of being frequented by many animals. He then placed his quivers under his head as a pillow and his bow under his feet and lay still, pretending to be dead.

For a long time Oniyeye lay perfectly still. Gradually, however, being on the ground and being a skilled hunter, he was able to discern movements in the undergrowth of the forest, sounds that were not made by the wind. Suddenly a tiny field mouse appeared and watched Oniyeye for a long time from a little distance, then, growing bolder, he came up close to the hunter and looked again. All this while Oniyeye kept his eyes closed and pretended to be dead. Now the field mouse had often been warned about Oniyeye and of his great skill as a hunter.

He was well known to all the creatures of the forest, who were quick to inform each other if he was hunting in the district. They always knew Oniyeye by his talisman.

The field mouse started to sing and call all the other animals to come and witness that the greatest of all hunters, Oniyeye, was dead and peace and safety had once more returned to the forest. He was soon heard by the monkeys, and their loud chattering attracted other animals. So one by one all the animals from the district gathered in the glade till it was full, and there was great rejoicing among them. Not only the animals, but the birds and insects too gathered to celebrate the good news. Returning to their homes, they called on all their companions to go and look at the corpse of Oniyeye lying in the glade and spread the report that he was dead.

The animal with one hundred and fifty-two tails learned the news from some birds that happened to be flying home across the hollow mountain, chirping with joy. He called one of the birds and asked him if the news was correct. "Go and see for yourself," replied the bird. "You will see all the other animals around the hunter's body in the glade."

"Good, go back and announce to the animals that I, the animal of one hundred and fifty-two

136

tails, am coming to witness Oniyeye's death, and tell them to prepare for my coming."

The bird flew back and informed the others, so the hunter knew his plan had worked.

Coming down from his hollow mountain, the animal with one hundred and fifty-two tails went to the glade. When he appeared, all the other animals were impressed, and prostrating themselves on the ground, hailed him as their king.

"This is a great day for all of us," said the king of the animals. "This man Oniyeye was the most powerful hunter in the world and because of him, my friends, I have shut myself up alone in the hollow mountain for many years. Now that I have witnessed his death I will come down, and henceforth I will live here in the forest among you all." There was a roar of applause at these words, and the animals took their king to see the hunter's body.

Then the king started to boast of his great power. "Now pick up the dead Oniyeye," ordered the animal of one hundred and fifty-two tails, "and carry him back to my hollow mountain while I mount him like a horse and ride home in triumph."

At these words, Oniyeye sprang up, seizing his bow and arrows as he did so. There was a great cry of astonishment and fear from every-

138

body, and instead of staying to help their king, the animals fled in confusion into the forest. As for the animal with one hundred and fifty-two tails, he lay there quivering before the hunter.

Oniyeye was about to kill the animal, but he begged the hunter to spare his life and said he would become his slave and work for him for the rest of his life.

So Oniyeye spared him and carried him back to King Olu Dotun.

There was great excitement and rejoicing when they reached the king's palace, and people came from far and wide to witness the strange animal with so many tails.

As for the other hunters, some had been able to find animals with as many as fifty tails and one hunter had even found one with one hundred tails. King Olu Dotun had, however, particularly announced that he would give his daughter in marriage to the man who produced one with one hundred and fifty-two. So Oniyeye married the king's daughter and was given half the kingdom to rule over. As for the animal of one hundred and fifty-two tails, he lived peacefully in captivity, and the other animals of the forest enjoyed greater security, for Oniyeye did not go hunting so often after his marriage.

Kin Kin and the Cat

Kin Kin is the smallest of all the birds in the
forest and thinks an immense amount of himself, in spite of his tiny size. There was a time
when Kin Kin was not popular with the other
birds of the forest, and the wild animals did not
care for him either. Kin Kin was perfectly
aware of this, but it did not trouble him very
much, for he went his own way and pleased himself. The wild cat, like Kin Kin, was also un-
popular because he behaved in a similar manner,
never turning up at the meetings held by the
chiefs, and always hunting by himself. One
would have thought that, having so much in
common and both being despised by their communities, they would have been friends, but this
was not the case. In fact, Kin Kin and the cat
went out of their way to be unpleasant to each
other whenever they happened to find themselves hunting in the same part of the forest.

One day, the king of the animals, who at that

time was very friendly with the king of the birds, decided that he would make his subjects clear and prepare a new farm for him in the heart of the forest. The king of the birds hearing this, offered his help too. He sent his birds to find a suitable area, and he promised that they should help the animals with the work of preparation.

So all the animals, with of course the exception of the cat, who had taken himself off, set to work preparing the king's farm, and all the birds with the exception of Kin Kin, who had not been asked, flew along to help.

Soon they had prepared a very large clearing in the forest. Part of the land was burned and prepared for a crop of yams. Another area was prepared for corn, and then the birds helped the animals to do the planting.

Kin Kin had watched these preparations from a cotton tree. Although he had no desire to help the others he was at the same time furious that he had not been asked to help. The cat had also watched the preparations unseen.

When all was prepared and the king of the animals was due to inspect the work, Kin Kin sang a song to the king of the forest:

> O forest king, see what the animals and birds
> have done!

141

The trees are uprooted, the ground is cleared.
The king of the animals is planting his farm in
  your domain.
Retrieve what is yours: make the weeds grow.
Make the grasses close over what should be
  yours.

When Kin Kin had finished, sure enough, the royal farm had vanished from sight.

The next day the king of the animals was unable to find the farm, and he ordered the animals and birds to commence their work all over again.

Once again the work was commenced and finished, and the day before the king was due to inspect the finished work, Kin Kin returned and sang as before, and so again the king's farm vanished, and the spot was overgrown as before.

Again the animals and birds patiently set to work, and for a third time Kin Kin sang to the forest king and destroyed their work.

"This must be the work of Kin Kin," said the cat to himself, but he said nothing to the others and greatly enjoyed the annoyance it caused.

The farm was prepared again, and this time it was decided to appoint a watchman to keep an eye open for the culprit. The leopard was elected by the Council of Animals to do this. He watched all the next day, but it was very hot and towards evening he fell asleep. It was then that Kin Kin sang to the forest king, and when the leopard awoke he was hardly able to free himself from the tangled undergrowth.

Each fresh destruction of his farm only made the king of the animals more determined than ever to complete the work and find the culprit, but whoever was chosen to watch, the result was always the same, because Kin Kin waited patiently for his chance, which always came sooner or later.

The cat was now sure that Kin Kin was responsible for the damage, and he saw a chance to further his own ends. Going to the king of the animals, he volunteered to keep watch the next time the farm was completed. He did not, being a wise animal, say who the culprit was; and the king, although he was surprised at the cat's offer, was glad to accept it.

The cat set off quietly to the royal farm. He hunted around until at last he saw Kin Kin sitting on a leafy branch overlooking the farm, patiently waiting for the animals and birds to complete their work. Before Kin Kin could sing his magic song to the forest king, the cat had pounced on him and devoured him.

So the grass and weeds did not grow again on the royal farm. Next morning, when all the ani-

mals and birds had come along, half expecting
that they would have to commence their work
all over again, they and the king of the animals
were very glad to find the farm in good order.
Calling the cat, they inquired who had been responsible for the mischief.

"You need not bother," replied the cat. "I
have eaten him and the royal farm is safe." The
cat saw that everybody was curious to know
who was responsible, and he took great pleasure
in keeping the secret of Kin Kin to himself.
"One day," he thought, "I might find it useful
to sing to the forest king myself." The king
thanked the cat for the good work, but he was
very angry with the animal's obstinacy.

Now the leopard and those animals who had
failed to keep watch were annoyed at their
failure and bore the cat a grudge. The leopard
came forward to the king.

"I do not believe the cat's story, O king," he
said. "He refuses to say whom he ate, and he
took no part in the work of preparing your royal
farm. He has long been a master of juju and I
am of the opinion that by his magic he was the
one who destroyed our work so often. Now he
pretends to have eaten the culprit, with the idea
of gaining your confidence and seeking favors.
The answer is that he has eaten nobody and he
is the mischief-maker, and a liar besides."

There were great cries of agreement from the other watchmen who had failed, and, as nobody liked the cat, the cry was soon taken up by all the animals and birds. "Kill him—kill him," they all cried. The cat, seeing that everybody had turned against him and that he was not going to be given a chance of a hearing to clear himself and put the blame on the dead Kin Kin, took himself off in a great hurry to the nearest town. He cursed himself for having eaten the whole of Kin Kin, without leaving a portion as evidence to show the others. It was a very long time indeed before he ventured out into the forest again.

The Funeral of the Forest King

After the death of Kin Kin and the hurried departure of the cat for the town, there was peace for a very long time among the animals and birds. The forest king allowed the king of the animals to maintain the farm, and the birds and the animals to use his domains, where they roamed about and hunted to their heart's content.

Then one day the forest king died. A great council of all the animals was called, and it was decided that the forest king, because of his great kindness to all animals, must be given the finest funeral ever to be witnessed in the land. The animals had a long discussion about the ceremonies and the form that they should take. It was at last decided that a large drum should be constructed for the occasion and beaten throughout the ceremonies, which were to be long and elaborate.

Somebody suggested that they should draw

146

lots for an animal to be sacrificed to the forest king: the skin of the animal selected was to be used for the construction of the drum. The roan had a much better idea. He suggested that, as all the animals had benefited by the kindness of the dead forest king, they should therefore all contribute a small portion of their ears. From the pieces, which were to be sewn together by a tailor from the town, a drum could be constructed. This idea was adopted; and so all the animals contributed portions of their ears. The eliri, the smallest of all rats, also contributed his share, but the others laughed at him and refused to take it when they saw what a tiny portion it was. The eliri, who had in actual fact contributed quite a large portion of his tiny ears, was furious at this insult, and took himself off to sulk alone.

When all the pieces of the animals' ears had been carefully collected, the cat suddenly reappeared. This was his first visit to the forest since his hurried departure after the murder of Kin Kin, and he informed everybody that he had come to pay his last respects to the forest king. Nobody, although they disliked him as much as ever, felt they were in a position to refuse his request, and he was told he would be welcomed by all provided he returned to the town and

147

brought a tailor to sew the ears together, because he was the animal best acquainted with the town. The cat promised to do this, and on the following day he returned with a tailor who sewed the pieces of ears together. When this was completed, the cat, who, of course, had not contributed even the smallest portion of his own ears towards the drum, fetched a drum-maker from the town, and soon the skin was stretched tightly over it and all was ready for the great ceremony to begin. In the meantime, the eliri, who had taken the animals' insult very badly, had made up his mind to report the matter to the gods. He was overjoyed when they answered his prayers. They informed him he might call for any assistance he required to help punish the animals. The eliri, on hearing this, thanked the gods and said he did not wish to bother them, but, if they were willing to grant him the assistance of Ayan, the god of the drum, he would be more than satisfied. To this the god Ayan agreed and the eliri then told him what he wanted him to do.

When the funeral ceremony was due to commence, all the animals gathered about the drum, but to everyone's astonishment no sound could be got from it. Although all those present tried hard to beat it, none of them could produce a sound and, after a great deal of trying on everybody's part, they left the drum in disgust and proceeded with the rest of the ceremonies, which were very disappointing, however, without the sound of the drum. As the funeral procession of the dead forest king moved away, everybody was startled to hear the deep sound of the drum. Now, the eliri, who had been hiding in the bush close by, had crawled out and calling on Ayan to help him, succeeded where the others had failed. When the animals heard the drumming they came rushing back, but the eliri heard them coming and hid himself. Again they all tried to sound the drum, but with no more success than before.

Each time the funeral procession of the dead forest king attempted to move off, the animals would hear the drum sound, but each time they returned, they found it silent and the place deserted.

At last, exasperated, they decided to place a guard by the drum to see what was happening. While the guard watched the drum was silent, but if he looked away from it the drumming would commence.

"The eliri is not present at the ceremonies, I notice," said the cat to himself. "I wonder if he has anything to do with this drumming?"

When the next guard was due to be chosen, the cat volunteered and was selected by the other animals. Slowly and deliberately he stretched himself out by the drum to watch and wait. Presently, when all was silent, the eliri appeared. Catching sight of the cat he tried to run away into the bush, but the cat was too quick for him, and he was caught and killed, and the cat ate him so that nothing remained of the tiny eliri.

After the ceremonies were over, all the animals returned to the drum and the cat. "What has happened?" they asked.

"I have eaten the drummer," replied the cat.

"Who was the drummer?" they all shouted,

but the cat just sat perfectly still and refused to tell them. Again they all tried to beat the drum but no sound would come forth.

"It is no use trying to beat the drum. I have already told you the drummer is dead, and the drum will never sound again," replied the cat.

"Long ago I told all you animals that this cat was a mischief-maker, a liar, and an animal with knowledge of a great juju. Now he has deceived us all into thinking somebody beats the drum and, as once before, he will not tell us who that somebody really is," the leopard roared.

"He is not fit to dwell in the Land of the Animals, and we must drive him back to the Town of Man," shouted all the animals.

At this the cat spat at the animals, and, with a great bound, he jumped clear of their circle and took himself off at great speed to the town.

Since that day, the cat has continued to live by himself in the homes of men. He still eats birds and mice when he can catch them, and all other animals either chase him or ignore him when they see him. His only friends are men, and even they find him secretive and strange. As for the drum, it never sounded again, and not long after the forest king's death, the white ants destroyed it.

Ahoro and His Wife Etipa

At a town called Imesi there lived, in the early days of the Yoruba people, a man called Ahoro, who was strong enough to destroy a man's house. People were afraid of Ahoro; but he kept to himself and lived apart from his fellow men. Ahoro was not alone, however, for with him as his only companion was his wife Etipa.

Ahoro and Etipa had been living together for some time when one day a quarrel arose between them over some trivial matter. Neither would give way to the other and both continued in their stubborn ways. At last it was decided to refer the matter to the chief of Imesi, who was a man renowned for his patience and tact in settling the inevitable village squabbles. In spite of this, however, the Chief of Imesi was unable to bring about a reconciliation between Ahoro and his wife Etipa, and so the man and wife parted. Etipa took herself off to find a hus-

band and a home in Imesi, while Ahoro remained alone.

It was a dangerous thing, however, for a man
of Imesi to marry the woman who had lived
with the powerful Ahoro. One day he might
come and reclaim her, and his great strength
was well known to everybody. Etipa was very
beautiful to look upon, but, in spite of this, the
villagers would have nothing to do with her, and
at last, not finding either a husband or a home,
she left Imesi and went out to live in the bush.
Here poor Etipa found no rest either. She fell
sick and the insects and other pests of the bush
gave her no respite or peace of mind, and it was

not long before she realized that the bush could not become her home any more than Imesi. Etipa therefore returned to the town and sought the advice of an Ifa priest.

"The gods are annoyed with your and your husband's stubbornness. You cannot live apart; your place is with your husband Ahoro, and not in Imesi or the bush," he told Etipa. "Now," continued the Ifa priest, "you will return to live with your husband and the gods will see to it that you quarrel no more with each other, but live together in silent peace away from the abodes of men." So Etipa returned to Ahoro.

They welcomed each other, and ever since that

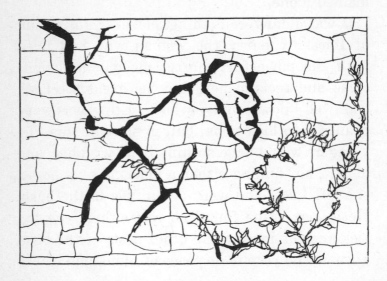

time they have lived happily and in peace with each other, for the gods punished them in a strange way.

Ahoro became a ruin and the father of decay, pulling down and slowly destroying the homes of men. As for Etipa, she was turned into the small, green plant that grows amid the ruins of broken walls.

The Orphan Boy
and the Magic Twigs

Ajao was an orphan. His father and mother had died when he was a little boy of five years of age. His father's brother then became his guardian, but unfortunately, three years later, Ajao's uncle died too and a friend of his uncle's, a man called Ogunmode, undertook to look after him.

Ajao was a very quiet little boy, and Ogunmode grew very fond of him and treated him as if he were his own son, for Ogunmode had no children of his own. Unfortunately for Ajao, Ogunmode was married to a very jealous woman, and when she saw how fond her husband grew of the boy, she did everything in her power to make Ajao's life wretched and miserable. When she was alone with him she would beat him and give him all the hardest jobs to do. Then when her husband returned, she would complain about the boy, saying that he was lazy and dirty and insolent to her in her husband's absence.

Life continued to be miserable for Ajao, and

as he grew up conditions in Ogunmode's house grew worse. When Ajao was nearly twenty, Ogunmode, persuaded by his wife, drove him from his house and told him that he would never help him again and that he was not to return.

Ajao now had no friends to support him. Nobody was willing to buy him materials to set him up as a trader or farmer, and he was forced to beg his food. Then one day the house of a rich trader was burgled and the townspeople accused the unfortunate Ajao of having committed the crime. In great fear he was forced to fly from the town to save himself from the hands of the angry mob.

Ajao now possessed nothing in the world except his loin cloth, and found life so wretched and unbearable that he decided to end it. As he had fled from the town, he had noticed a long piece of rope lying on the path, dropped, no doubt, by some passing trader. This he picked up for no special reason, but the idea now entered his head that he would hang himself with it.

For some time the unhappy boy wandered around, looking for a suitable tree to which he could tie the rope. At last, after wandering far into the bush, he saw a large branch that would do for his purpose. He climbed up, and was about to fling the rope around the limb of the tree, when something caught his attention. Between the masses of green foliage he saw a large town. "That is very strange," said Ajao, forgetting his miserable state and gazing at the town, "I never knew a town existed in that direction. Nobody has ever spoken about it that I can recollect." As he looked he became aware of something strange about the town. He could see the houses and streets quite plainly from where he sat in the branches, but there appeared to be no people moving about. All was silent and deserted and there was no sign of smoke; at the same time, it was swept and tidy and looked as if people lived there.

Ajao suddenly made up his mind to go and visit the place. "At least it will do no harm," he thought, "and perhaps I may find some work there and make a fresh start to my life." So, Ajao, leaving his rope, climbed down from the tree and set off through the bush in the direction of the town.

He had not gone very far when he came across an antelope. He was surprised when, instead of running away, it stood and watched him. Ajao was not armed, but in any case he felt that it would have been a mistake to have killed the animal. So, Ajao took no notice and walked on in the direction of the town. Presently he came to a bush track. Suddenly he heard a voice calling, "Ajao, Ajao! Where are you going?" He was very surprised at hearing his name called and looked around in the direction of the sound; he could see nobody. Then, as he stood still and waited, the antelope appeared. It was the animal who had spoken to him. "Where are you going to, Ajao?" it asked again.

"I saw a strange town from the top of a tree a few paces back," replied Ajao, who was now rather frightened.

"You must not go to that town you saw from the magic tree. That is the Town of the Animals, and this is the Country of the Animals. You must return quickly to the land of the sons of men, for you do not belong to us," said the antelope.

Ajao was now very afraid and confused, and he did not know what to do. He turned back, walked a few paces, and then sat down on a large rock to think what he should do next. "Shall I go back to the tree and hang myself, or go forward to the town and see what happens in this strange land, or stay here and starve?" Ajao asked himself.

But he was now very tired and he decided to lie down and sleep till darkness had come, and then he would go on and investigate the Town of the Animals. "If there is any danger, I can escape in the darkness and they will not see me," he thought to himself.

So Ajao lay down and slept. When he awoke it was already dark, and only the stars lit the narrow track. Ajao got up, stretched himself, and then made his way cautiously forward towards the town. The only sound came from the toads and the crickets.

The animals in this town dwelled in three separate communities. These were the Flesh-Eating Community, the Grass-Eaters, and the Reptiles. Although they all lived on friendly terms with one another they kept very much to their own communities.

Ajao crept up to the town quietly, and seeing a large mud building with lights inside, he crept up to the windows and gazed in. The approach to the building was through some bushes and he could not be seen.

Ajao had chosen that part of the town in which the Grass-Eating Community dwelled, and the building he had chosen to creep up to was none other than their meeting-house. The Grass-Eating animals were holding a meeting. As Ajao listened at the open windows, the various animals were speaking about their strength and powers in the art of medicine.

"My friends," said a huge elephant, slowly rising, "if you would all be kind enough to step outside for a few minutes, I will show you some great magic I can perform." As he spoke, he picked up a small bundle of twigs with his trunk and walked outside. In front of the building there was a large open place, all swept and clean. Here all the Grass-Eaters gathered and Ajao was able to watch them from around the corner of the building. The animals were too engrossed in watching the elephant to pay attention to anything else.

"Now look carefully, and stand back and give me plenty of room," said the elephant. He picked up one of the twigs, broke it in two and threw it into the circle of animals. Immediately there sprang up a large building. There were sounds of approval from all the animals, and they trooped inside to inspect the building. When they

had all entered, the elephant, who now stood inside, took another twig and broke it. When he threw it to the ground, the house disappeared as suddenly as it had appeared, leaving the astonished animals standing close together where a room had been.

"That is very wonderful indeed, but if all my brothers will stand back and give me room, I will show you a trick at least as good," said a voice that sounded familiar to Ajao. As he looked and listened he recognized the antelope who had spoken to him earlier in the day.

The animals formed a circle again and, picking up another twig, he broke it and threw it on the ground. It turned into bags of cowrie shells. Another twig was broken and the cowrie shells disappeared.

So one by one the Grass-Eating animals came forward into the circle and by means of breaking a stick produced something, and then by the breaking of a second twig made the object disappear. Some produced fine cloth, others jams and foodstuffs, and others again produced fine beads and jewels. There seemed to be no end to the objects they could produce by means of the sticks. Ajao, who had eaten nothing all day, was most interested in the magic twigs that

163

produced the food, and he took good care to note where the animals threw those twigs after the display had finished.

The animals' meeting continued all through the night, but as the first signs of light began to appear in the sky the hungry, watching Ajao was pleased to see the meeting breaking up and the animals returning to their homes.

When all was silent and deserted, Ajao darted forward, and picking up one of the sticks which had produced the food, he ran swiftly back into the bush until he was far from the town. Breaking a tiny piece off the twig, he was very pleased to find a magnificent feast spread out on the ground in front of him, and he ate to satisfaction.

By means of the twig Ajao was able to live alone in the bush and supply himself with food and drinks. Each day he would break off a tiny piece of twig. As each day passed, Ajao's twig grew smaller, and so each night he would creep up to the town of the animals in the hope that he would find them holding another meeting and breaking more magic twigs. He was unsuccessful, however, for the Grass-Eating Community's meeting-house remained deserted.

"I must try another part of the town," thought Ajao to himself, "for I have now only sufficient twig to last another two days."

The following night, Ajao crept around to the far side of the town, and as he reached the fringe of the bush, he saw a large gathering of animals sitting around a fire. As he crept up and listened, he saw a leopard addressing the meeting.

"My friends and brothers of the Flesh-Eating Community of this town, not long ago at a meeting of the Grass-Eating Community, I hear that many acts of magic were performed by the animals of that community. Word has now gone round this town that only those of the Grass-Eating Community are able to perform acts of magic, and that they possess more powerful jujus than any of us."

There were angry cries of, "No, this is not true," and, "Let us demonstrate the power of our medicine and jujus."

"I hear that magic was performed by breaking certain twigs," said a lion.

"Just so," continued the leopard. "Certain twigs were broken by the Grass-Eaters at the meeting of their chiefs. Now, my friend the dog has brought along some magic twigs, and we too will show this town that the chiefs of the Flesh-Eaters possess considerable skill and powerful jujus and medicines." There were growls of approval from all the Flesh-Eaters.

Exactly the same thing happened as at the

previous meeting of the Grass-Eaters. One by one the Flesh-Eaters came forward and broke twigs to produce a rich variety of things and then broke a second twig to make them disappear again.

Ajao watched carefully when the animal broke the twig that produced food, and noted carefully where the twig was thrown after the experiment.

It was a successful meeting, and it broke up just before dawn. All the Flesh-Eaters were immensely pleased with themselves and felt that they had produced magic to equal that of the Grass-Eaters.

When all was quiet, Ajao collected the twig he required, and ran back to his hiding place in the bush and lived as before. Ajao was very fond of honey cakes and he always made a point of asking to be supplied with them before he broke a piece of the magic twig. His wishes were always granted. He had now learned that the animals lived in three communities and each night he would go off to search around the outskirts of the town of the animals. "The Reptiles will probably hold a meeting soon, and they too are certain to break twigs," he thought. "I must keep a watch for their meeting." Each night he would set out to look and watch, taking with him some honey cakes wrapped up in leaves, to eat while he waited.

The day following the meeting of the Flesh-Eating animals, the dog happened to pass the place where they had broken the twigs. As he looked and smelled around, he was surprised to notice that the twigs had been tampered with and there was a strange smell. Seaching around he discovered the naked footprints of Ajao. "Ah," said the dog, "as I thought, the son of man has been around." The dog immediately ran off to tell the other Flesh-Eating animals and a hurried meeting was called. The Flesh-Eaters reported the matter to the Grass-Eaters and the antelope came forward and told them about his meeting with Ajao in the bush and said that the footprints they discovered probably belonged to him. Both communities decided to post animals around their town to keep a sharp lookout for the boy. It was therefore not surprising that Ajao was caught one night as he came prowling around the animals' town. A large monkey caught him, and he was dragged into the town. An extraordinary meeting of all the Grass- and Flesh-Eating animals was called to see the son of man, and to decide what to do with the uninvited visitor to the Town of the Animals.

"Let us see this son of man who comes uninvited to our land," cried some. "Kill him—kill him," cried some of the Flesh-Eating Community. "Let the elephant trample on him," yelled some of the Grass-Eaters.

All seemed determined that poor Ajao should die. The boy lay on the ground where the monkey had flung him. "Let us see him first. He is called Ajao," said the antelope. "Hold Ajao up that we may see him," cried the crowd of animals.

The elephant picked up Ajao with his trunk and held him above all the animals. "Behold the son of man that comes to our town like a thief in the night," he bellowed.

Now Ajao had been clutching his honey cakes tied up in leaves all this time, and as the elephant opened his mouth to speak, he quickly untied the bundle and threw a honey cake into the open mouth of the elephant. The elephant had never tasted a honey cake before and as he ate it he decided that he liked it very much. As he was a long time eating the cake the other animals were growing impatient.

"Throw him down. Throw him down. Let us kill him," they yelled.

"No," replied the elephant. "I will not throw him down. I suggest that this boy should be kept by us as a pet. He has just given me a most

168

delicious morsel of food to eat. I do not know what it is, but it tastes very good."

"Who ever heard of the son of man being kept as a pet by animals?" shouted some of the animals.

"Why, that is what man does to some of us," said the cat. "The idea is absurd."

"What does this food taste like? Let me try it," said the lion.

Gently, the elephant let Ajao down and placed him by the Chief of the Flesh-Eating Community. "See what a handsome boy he is," said the elephant. Ajao gave the lion a honey cake, and he ate it and he too was delighted with it.

"I agree with the elephant. The boy is handsome and it would be a shame to kill him. He must live with us and teach us how to make this food."

When the elephant and lion had decided that Ajao should live with the animals, most of the others were quick to agree with them. Those who were still doubtful were given the remaining honey cakes to eat and at once changed their minds.

So Ajao lived with the animals. He told them how unkind men had been to him, and how they had driven him out of their town and how he had then tried to hang himself. It was while doing this that he had noticed the Town of Animals, and had come exploring at night.

Ajao taught the animals how to avoid the traps set by hunters, and how and where to avoid men when they were out looking for meat, and which men could be trusted. He told them of the powers of spears and arrows, and when to fear them. The animals grew to love and trust Ajao, and he was soon treated like one of themselves and accepted into their circle. They taught him the magic of the twigs and they all ate honey cakes and were happy together. Ajao also met the Reptile Community and he made great friends with them too.

Ajao lived for several years with the three communities and then he began to grow restless. "I must return to my people," he told a meeting of the animals one day. None of them wanted him to go, but the lion said, "It is right that Ajao should leave us and return to his own people. It is time that he had a wife and children. He has become our very good friend, and will never betray us to men when he returns to their country. Ajao, we will be sorry to see you depart. You are the only son of man who has ever lived with us as one of ourselves, and we trust and love you. If your own people ever treat you badly, return to us and we will always be ready to help you. Take some of the magic twigs with you. They will help you to begin life again in the world of man."

All the animals and reptiles came to say good-bye to Ajao and they accompanied him to the border of their country.

"Come back and see us one day, Ajao," they called to him as he waved back to them.

Ajao returned to the town he had once been driven from as if he were a thief. First he broke the elephant's twig and threw it on to a piece of open ground he had selected. A fine house sprang up on the spot. Then he continued to break sticks until he had sufficient clothes, goods, and food. Ajao was now a wealthy man and ready to start a new life.

Unfortunately, however, the people had not forgotten or forgiven Ajao and still looked upon him as a thief. Whispers began to spread from the marketplace. "Look, Ajao has returned with his loot to live amongst us. How could he honestly have acquired all this wealth in such a short time?"

Not long after his arrival a large crowd came to his house, thinking Ajao had been stealing from other towns during his absence, and dragged him off to the chiefs' court.

Here Ajao was asked by the chiefs to explain

how he had acquired his great wealth, but he was afraid to tell them the story of the animals and the magic twigs, fearing what they might do to him. Also he remembered his promise to his animal friends. Having failed to explain satisfactorily to the court how he came by all his possessions, he was sent to prison and all his goods were confiscated.

They kept poor Ajao in prison for a long time, and when at last he was released, he again set out for the Town of the Animals, as he had done several years before, a beggar. "This time there is this difference," thought Ajao to himself, "I have good friends where I am going."

Ajao was not disappointed. When he returned to the animals there was great rejoicing and a large meeting of the Grass-Eaters, the Flesh-Eaters, and the Reptiles was called. To them Ajao explained matters, and the three communities held separate sessions and after this Ajao was summoned to appear before the three leaders—the lion, the elephant, and the crocodile.

"We have considered your words carefully, Ajao, and because of your loyalty to us in not divulging to man the secrets of your power, we now give you our permission and blessing to return once again to the town of your people, and explain before the king and the chiefs the secrets of the twigs and the powers we have bestowed on you." So Ajao took another bundle of magic twigs and returned.

This time he went directly to the king and on being admitted to his presence, saluted him and said, "O king, you know well your subject Ajao, who has twice been accused of being a thief by the people and who was driven from this town after being put in prison and had all his goods taken from him. You will remember that the last time he was here he refused to tell you the secret of his power and wealth, and your court ruled that he was a thief. This time I, Ajao, return with permission from those who gave it to me to explain my power. If you would therefore appoint a day on which you, the chiefs, and the people can assemble, you will witness many wonderful things, and I think I can clear my name and satisfy the court of my innocence."

So the king appointed a day and the chiefs and many people came to the palace, and when all had gathered together, Ajao took his twigs and performed the magic. As the fine building, the rich cloth, the jewels and foods and drinks appeared before the astonished people, there were great cries of surprise. Everybody was very impressed and many, perceiving his great wealth, offered him their daughters in marriage. Ajao finally accepted the king's daughter to be his wife, and before the meeting ended, a day was arranged for the marriage ceremony. Ajao then announced that the members of the three communities which had helped him would also attend the ceremony.

As the day drew near there were great preparations and much excitement in the town. The night before the marriage was due to take place, the Grass-Eaters, Flesh-Eaters, and the Reptiles arrived, also many people from outlying towns and villages. There was much rejoicing and dancing.

It was a very dark night and as the animals came, one of them threw lines all about him, which immediately turned into lanterns, and the town streets were soon as bright as day. People were astonished at the magnificent rich apparel of the animals, which greatly surpassed that worn by the sons of man. The elephant's head was covered with a fine cap called an *abetiaja*, richly embroidered, which was afterwards copied by the sons of man. The lion wore a magnificent crown of beads, and the lizard a red fez which, incidentally, he wears to this day. The antelope was dressed in a beautiful gown, which he liked so much that he has continued to wear it ever since. The crocodile came in rich plush, and the boar in soft velvet. So all the animals and reptiles came in magnificent attire, which

174

astonished everybody, and like all the other luxuries for the wedding feast, it was all produced by means of the magic twigs. The night passed amid great rejoicing, feasting, and dancing, and the sons of man said they had never witnessed anything like it before.

On the morning of the marriage festival, the king presented his daughter and Ajao with a very fine coach called *keke elesin*. The animals, not to be outdone, caused a magnificent coach to be constructed and borne by eagles, and in this Ajao and the princess were borne over the heads of the crowd and paraded the town from dawn to dusk. Then the happy couple retired to their respective houses for the night. Early next morning, the princess was led to the house of Ajao and handed to him.

So ended the wonderful marriage of Ajao and the king's daughter, and the animals returned to their country in peace, and Ajao dwelt in great comfort in the Town of Man.

Some time after this, a son was born to Ajao and his parents called him Akano. When Akano had grown to be a fine boy, Ajao took him on a visit to the Country of the Animals, and they welcomed Ajao and Akano and the three communities feasted them in turn.

"When you first came amongst our people, Ajao, you were not much older than your son

Akano, and we taught you many things. Will you not leave Akano with us now so that he may grow up to know and understand the animals?" asked the old elephant.

"I am more than willing that that should be so," replied Ajao.

So Akano stayed with the animals and they taught him many things, and he learned to speak their languages and to understand their customs. Akano was very fond of his father and never tired of listening to the story of how his father first came to live in the Country of the Animals. The animals liked Akano very much, but still they would never explain the magic of the twigs to him, although he asked them many times.

"Only your father Ajao knows that secret among men, and when he dies no other man will ever know it," replied the old lion. "However, because of your father, if you are ever in any kind of trouble we will always help you," continued the old lion.

Akano lived with the animals many years and then one day he went to see the elephant. "Ah, Akano, I know why you have come to see me. Many years ago your father came just as you have come now. Do you wish to return to the land of your people?"

"I do," replied Akano.

A great feast was given in honor of Akano by the three communities that night, and on the following morning Akano set out for his home town with all the animals accompanying him. When they reached the frontier, the old elephant said, "Akano, we have never told you the magic of the twigs, but here is one magic twig as a parting gift for you. If you break it and wish for anything your wish will be granted."

Akano thanked them all and they left him with many good wishes for his grandfather, the old king, his father Ajao, and his mother.

Akano was sorry to leave all his friends in the Country of the Animals, but as he walked on towards his town his spirits rose. He had not seen his people for a long time and it would be nice to meet them all again. As he approached the town he was struck by the emptiness of the road and the lack of people, and Akano grew worried. "I should have returned earlier," he said to himself.

When Akano reached the open country above the Town of Man he saw the reason for the silence. Only blackened crumbling ruins remained where once the Town of Man had stood. The whole town had been utterly destroyed. Akano wandered about until he reached the ruins of his grandfather's palace and his father's home, then, remembering the magic twig the old elephant had given him, he took it quickly and broke it, wishing that the town could be rebuilt and his people could return.

Immediately the town was rebuilt and he saw some people wandering through the streets. Calling them, Akano asked of his family and what had befallen them.

"Alas, Akano," they replied, "you come back with your magic twigs from the Country of the Animals to find the Town of Man has been destroyed by a neighboring tribe. Your grandfather the king and your father Ajao were slain in the battle, and your mother was carried off into captivity by the raiders. Many people were killed, but many have fled to the bush for safety."

Akano then ordered the drummers and trumpeters to sound and summon the people back to the town he had rebuilt by means of the elephant's magic twig. When they had returned, Akano was proclaimed the new king.

When Akano had restored the Town of Man as far as he was able, he hastened back to the Country of the Animals and reported the matter to the council of the three communities, and asked them to assist him in waging war on the tribe that had destroyed his family and his town.

"We grieve for what has happened to you and

your people, Akano, and we will mourn the sad loss of your father, Ajao, whom we loved and who was the friend of all animals and reptiles, but we cannot wage war on man, Akano. However, we will do all in our power to help you recover your mother. Beyond that we cannot help you. Return now to the Town of Man and gather your soldiers together and wait for us, and you will see how we can help you," said the old elephant.

So Akano thanked the elephant, the lion, and the crocodile, and returned to the Town of Man. He collected his soldiers together and waited to see what would happen next.

Slowly but surely, Akano's enemies were surrounded by the animals and reptiles of the three communities. They did not fight them, but they closed in gradually on all sides. First the Grass-Eaters came and devoured the crops of the tribe. When the people came out to look for food, they were devoured by the Flesh-Eaters and attacked by the Reptiles. Gradually all the food disappeared from the markets, and finally, they were forced to sue for peace and release Akano's mother, who returned to the Town of Man and lived peacefully with her son the king.

Tintinyin and the Unknown King
of the Spirit World

A very long time ago there once lived in Yorubaland a boy called Tintinyin. His father had
died when he was a small child and his mother
followed his father to the next world a few years
later. Tintinyin had nobody to care for him and
he grew up alone and uncared for. He had made
his home in the bush among the wild animals
and birds, and they had fed and clothed him,
looked after him, and brought him up. It was
not surprising, therefore, that Tintinyin was
able to understand the language of the birds and
the animals as well as he understood Yoruba.

Not very far from the part of the bush in
which Tintinyin dwelled, there was a large town
ruled by a powerful Oba, and every year a great
annual festival took place there. Tintinyin always attended the festival, for he liked the
dancing, singing, and drumming, and the fine
robes the people wore for the occasion. The Oba
was a wonderful-looking man too, and greatly

impressed Tintinyin when, attended by his chiefs, soldiers, and peoples, he took part in the annual festivals. Tintinyin also went because there was always plenty to eat and drink.

In those far-distant times it was said that the unknown king of the Spirit World would always come down to earth to attend the annual festivals held in the Oba's town. Nobody could recognize him, however, because he always came disguised as an ordinary citizen, and after the ceremonies were over he would return to the Spirit World as unobtrusively as he had come.

Now the Oba was anxious to test the truth of this belief, and so just before the annual festival was due to commence he sent his bellmen out to

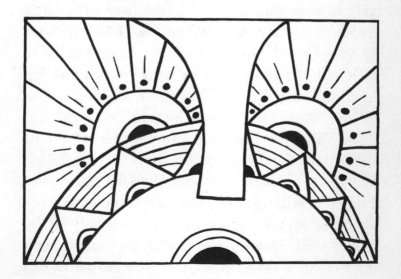

announce to the people that if any of them could distinguish the unknown king of the Spirit World and point him out to the Oba at the annual festival, he would be rewarded with many valuable gifts and given a high position in the town.

When Tintinyin heard the bellmen's message he went straight to the Oba's palace and announced to the Oba that he was willing to point out the king of the Spirit World to him. Tintinyin, in actual fact, had no idea what the Spirit King looked like, and could certainly not have picked him out from amongst the great crowd that attended the festival. But he was sure that somehow or other the animals or birds would be able to help him. When the Oba heard the boy's words and saw how small and wretched he was, he was very doubtful about the boy's ability to pick out the king, and by way of frightening him, and stopping the boy from making a fool of him before his subjects, he told Tintinyin that if he failed to keep his promise he would be taken and sacrificed to the king of the Spirit World as a punishment. To the Oba's surprise, Tintinyin still insisted that he could pick out the Spirit King, and said he was quite ready to die if he failed. Then he left the Oba's palace, leaving behind a very astonished Oba seated on his throne. "That boy is strange," he remarked.

On the day of the festival, Tintinyin arrived to find everybody taking a lively interest in him. Word had gone around about Tintinyin's offer to the Oba, and many were curious to see what would happen. Others felt sorry for Tintinyin, and feared that the boy's life must be forfeited.

The Oba was seated on his throne, which had been placed in the cool shade made by the wide branches of a great tree. Tintinyin was called for and he went up to him and paid his respects. "Now boy, point out the unknown king of the Spirit World as you promised," said the Oba.

Since Tintinyin had last spoken to the Oba he had been very worried. Although he had consulted all the birds and animals he had been shown no sign whereby he could recognize the unknown king of the Spirit World on the great day.

Tintinyin was now beginning to wonder what he should do next, and for the first time he grew afraid. If he tried to run away to his friends, the animals and birds in the bush, the Oba's attendants would catch him long before he could make good his escape. He now felt he had been foolish, and wished he had never made such a rash promise to the Oba. How much better it would have been if he had only stayed in the bush, Tintinyin said to himself. As he stood before the Oba thinking, Tintinyin's eyes suddenly caught sight of a small ega bird. The bird was singing, and although nobody could understand its song Tintinyin was able to follow every word the bird sang.

> Tintinyin, O Tintinyin, you have spoken a word
>   too big for your mouth.
> You said you knew of the Spirit World's king.
>   The king of the dead and devils
> You know not. Now have you bartered your
>   young life away,
> For the Oba's special gifts. I will not let you die.
> Look forth along the line of my pointed right
>   wing. Alone stands a man there.
> No attributes or ornaments to his tattered gar-
>   ments show he is king,
> Yet he leans on a staff. Tintinyin, this is the
>   king,
> King of the Spirit World, and son, I am your
>   father.

So Tintinyin knew that his father had spoken to him through the voice of the ega and was helping him in his difficulty, and he was very glad.

The Oba was waiting. "Come, boy," he commanded, "I am waiting for you to show me the king of the Spirit World."

Tintinyin went directly to the old man leaning on a staff and clad in tattered garments and led him before the Oba. When the people saw this some of them laughed and thought the boy was foolish, and many said that he was making fun of the old man.

When the old man came before the Oba he pulled up his garment and displayed a tiny bead tied to a band around his ankle. This was the symbol of the unknown Spirit King. The king spoke no words to the Oba, Tintinyin, or the people, but having displayed his symbol, he quietly vanished from sight.

The Oba kept his promise and rewarded Tintinyin, and when he grew up he became a rich and powerful man.

Nobody ever saw the king of the Spirit World at the annual festival again, and no Oba since that time has ever asked to see him. But people still say that he comes every year, clad in the clothes of a poor man.

The Wise Dog

A strange thing once occurred in the Country of the Animals. There came a period of great strife and trouble, with many bitter fights and much hardship. Everything seemed to go wrong. It was as if a great curse had descended on all of them.

The king of the animals called a great meeting. Something must be done to put things right. All the animals were agreed on this point, but what were they to do, and what was the cause of their misfortunes? They argued over the matter for a very long time; many suggestions were put forward, but no conclusions were reached. Then somebody (nobody afterwards could say who had made the suggestion in the first place) suggested that all their troubles could be traced back to the days of their early youth, and if anybody were to be blamed it must be their mothers. Yes, their mothers were to blame for the whole thing. Had they not been

186

responsible for bringing them up? Had they not allowed them to play about when they should have been doing other things? Were their mothers not always interfering with them in the days of their youth? They had been a handicap all through. So the animals, seeking for a scapegoat on which to pin all their subsequent misfortunes, found one ready to hand in their mothers. The idea spread like a bush fire in the dry season. "We must kill all our mothers to punish them for our misfortunes and appease the gods," they all screamed. Every animal was to kill his own mother.

There was only one animal who was not carried away with this evil idea. He was the dog, who greatly respected his mother. He was too wise an animal to be carried away by their foolish words, but he had sufficient intelligence to see that it was hopeless to go against the wishes of all the other animals. So the dog quietly acquiesced to the idea of everybody killing off his own mother. The great slaughter of mothers commenced. The dog, fearing that if he hid his mother the other animals would discover her hiding place and slaughter them both, sent her to Heaven.

The dog's mother was very grateful for her son's kindness and consideration. When she was

about to depart, she told him that if ever he was in any trouble or want, he had only to call on her and she would help him. She then taught him a little song to sing when in trouble.

The animals were soon to know that the killing of their mothers had not helped matters very much, for the next season brought a terrible famine to the land. The waterholes dried up, and there was no meat, and all the crops failed, and many animals died.

The dog, remembering his mother's parting words, went out to a quiet and unfrequented part of the bush and sang:

O Mother, O Mother, send down your cord,
Take your son up to Heaven and feed him today.

For he needs your help now and remembers
  your words,
O please Mother, O Mother, O Mother!

Immediately a cord descended from Heaven and
on the end of it hung a tiny bench. The dog sat
himself down on the little bench and was pulled
up through the clouds to Heaven. When he
reached Heaven, his mother feasted him and
did everything she could to make him happy,
and when evening came he was let down again
into the starving Country of the Animals.

Each day while the famine lasted, the dog
would go and sing his song, and the cord would
descend and take him up to visit his mother in
Heaven.

One day, the tortoise, who was a friend of the
dog, met him.

"My friend," the tortoise remarked, "how is it
that you manage to look so sleek and fat in such
a dry and unhappy time? There is a severe
famine, the worst in living memory, and we are
all growing thin and feeble, yet you, I notice,
are getting fatter. Please tell me the reason
for it."

Now the dog was afraid that the tortoise
might remark on his good health to the other
animals, so he decided to let the tortoise in on his
secret. "Tortoise, if you promise never to tell

any of the other animals, I will let you into my great secret." The tortoise, like all people who are promised a share in a great secret, swore that he would tell nobody else. Alas, nature is a frail thing and probably the tortoise's intentions were as good as those of human beings who find themselves in a similar situation.

"Meet me at this place tomorrow morning at sunrise and I will show you," continued the dog.

At sunrise, the tortoise was waiting for the dog, and the dog came and sang to his mother as before, and again the cord with the tiny bench descended from Heaven and the dog and the tortoise sat on it and were hauled up into the sky by the dog's mother.

At sundown they descended, looking well fed and happy, the tortoise swearing by all things in Heaven and on earth that he would not divulge the dog's secret to any living animal.

A few days later the tortoise paid a visit to the king of the animals. "O great king, may I have a word with you privately?" he asked. The lion rose from his throne and motioned all the other animals to depart and leave them alone. "I have just come, great lion, from a place where there is no famine and one can eat to satisfaction," whispered the tortoise.

"Where is this place? I have not eaten a good meal for days, and I begin to hate this cursed country," replied the king.

"If you are willing to advance my position and interests in your kingdom, king of all animals, I will gladly tell you how we can reach this wonderful place," replied the tortoise as he peeped out at the king from under his shell.

"It shall be done, provided you keep your word. Make all the necessary arrangements for our departure, but keep it secret, tortoise," added the lion.

So the tortoise told the king to meet him at sunrise at a certain place. Needless to say the dog knew nothing about this arrangement. The following morning, the tortoise did not have to wait long at the rendezvous. In the gray light of dawn he saw the king coming and was greatly annoyed to find that he did not come alone. The king had brought not only his favorite wife, but also all his personal friends and followers. There was, in fact, quite a crowd of other animals.

"This is the last thing I wanted or expected," said the tortoise to himself, "but there is nothing I can do about it now, even if I take only the king up, all the others will witness it."

When the king arrived, the tortoise greeted

him and all his followers. Then he sang the dog's song and the cord with the tiny bench descended from the pale morning sky.

"How are we all going to sit on this tiny bench?" asked the king.

"We aren't," said the tortoise hurriedly. "There is only room for you and myself I fear; the others must remain behind."

"So be it," said the king, and he threw himself down on to the bench, and with great difficulty the tortoise was able to squeeze himself onto it too. The favorite wife and the king's followers were of a different opinion, however, for, as they saw the king and the tortoise ascending, they all rushed forward and as many as could flung themselves onto the rope.

Then there followed the most undignified scene imaginable. While the lion and the tortoise roared at them all to let go, the starving animals hung on with grim determination and took no notice of their king's orders. Some managed to clutch the cord, others, not so fortunate, hung on to the tails of the animals higher up, some even clutched at the lion's mane and others sat on the tortoise. A twisting, wriggling mass of angry, shouting animals slowly ascended into the sky.

193

The dog's mother, perceiving that something was amiss with the cord, peeped down from Heaven and saw all the animals ascending. "Mercy, they are all coming up to kill me," she declared, so quickly seizing a large knife, she cut the cord when they were halfway up to Heaven. There followed a great crash as they all fell to earth and were killed, with the exception of the tortoise, whose thick shell saved his life.

The animals from a nearby village, hearing the great crash of falling bodies, came out to investigate. They soon discovered that all the animals except the tortoise were dead, and it was not long before they recognized the dead body of the king. The tortoise was taken to the town to answer for the king's death. He told the whole story concerning the dog's mother and the cord that pulled them up to Heaven.

The animals would not believe his wonderful story, however, so he was led out to the spot where the king had died and beheaded for supposed crimes.

The dog later went back to sing to his mother to let down the cord. Alas, there was now no cord to let down. It only extended halfway, and so the dog was never again able to visit Heaven.

As the famine continued in the Country of the Animals, the dog took himself off to the Country

of Man, and ever since that time the dog has relied on man to feed him. Many men and animals have spent their lives wondering how the dog was able to send his mother to Heaven. Some suggested that he killed her as the other animals did, while others hold the view that somebody in Heaven must have let the cord down at his request. Alas, we shall never know the answer now, for the dog, having once shared a secret with fatal results, has never been caught out a second time.

The Wooden Spoon and the Whip

When famine once came to the land a certain man called Ajayi, finding there was nothing to eat in or near to his town, went farther afield in search of food. He came to a river and wandered along its bank till he came to an oil palm that overhung the river. Ajayi was overjoyed to find some palm nuts growing over the water. He climbed up the tree and out over the water and was just about to pick the palm nuts when they fell into the river. They all sank immediately except for one, which continued to float and was carried downstream. Ajayi climbed down from the tree and followed along the bank, all the time watching for the palm nut to be carried close in to the bank. However, it remained, bobbing up and down in the middle of the stream, and was slowly carried down to the sea.

Seeing that he was about to lose the one remaining nut, Ajayi took off his clothes and jumped into the sea, but as he reached it, the nut sank, and Ajayi, more determined than ever, dived down after it. The next moment a wonderful thing happened, for he suddenly found himself in a great palace under the sea, and there before him, in magnificent robes, sat Olokun, god of the sea.

"What brings you to my palace, Ajayi?" asked the sea god.

Ajayi explained how he had gone out to search for food and had found and followed a palm nut, which had led him before Olokun.

"Stay with me and I will see that you are fed," said Olokun.

"My family are starving at home," replied Ajayi.

The sea god stood up and going to a wooden

chest, which stood in one corner of his room, he opened it and brought out a strange-looking wooden spoon.

"Ajayi," he said, "take this wooden spoon back to your family and keep it safely, and you and your family will never want for food. All you have to do is to ask the spoon what its duty is, and it will always provide you with food."

Ajayi thanked the sea god for his great kindness, and having paid his respects, he was led out through one of the many passages that led off from Olokun's hall. Presently Ajayi found himself outside and standing on the seashore. He went home as quickly as he could and showed his family the wonderful spoon. "What is your duty?" Ajayi asked the spoon.

"To feed," replied the spoon, and immediately there was plenty of food prepared and ready for eating, and Ajayi and his family ate to satisfaction.

Ajayi was a good man and wanted to help his people. He went to the king and showed him the spoon. The king called all his people together and they all came and sat down in his compound and had as much food as they required.

Having fed all the people, the king and Ajayi next decided to feed all the starving animals, so

all the animals were summoned to the palace, and they all came and ate till their great hunger was satisfied.

At the end of the feast, a tortoise came up to Ajayi and asked him how he had managed to get the wonderful spoon. Ajayi related the story of the palm nut and how it had led him eventually to the sea god Olokun. The tortoise thanked Ajayi and then went off to the spoon and said, "What is your duty?"

"To feed," replied the spoon.

"Then get me a palm nut," replied the tortoise. Immediately a palm nut was placed before the tortoise. He picked it up, and having thanked the king, he left the palace.

The tortoise set out for the river, and when he reached the water's edge he threw the palm nut in and watched it as it floated slowly down towards the sea. The tortoise followed.

When the nut reached the sea, the tortoise dived in after it and followed it down as it sank. The next minute the tortoise found himself standing before the sea god Olokun.

"What brings you here, tortoise?" asked Olokun.

The tortoise related how he had seen some palm nuts growing on a tree by the river, and feeling hungry, he had tried to pick them, but they had suddenly fallen from the tree into the water and one had continued to float down-stream till it had led him before the sea god.

"Having come before me, what do you want?" demanded Olokun.

"I want you to give me a wooden spoon so that I can feed my starving family," replied the tortoise.

"I have no spoons left," replied the Sea God, getting up and opening his wooden chest. "However, since you have taken so much trouble to see me, I will give you a whip instead, and it will help you and your family for the rest of your lives."

The tortoise thanked Olokun for his great kindness and, taking the whip, he was led out through the passage till he found himself standing outside on the seashore. He hurried home, and going inside with his family, he locked the door to keep people from seeing his magic whip. "Now," said the tortoise, "I have as good a gift as Ajayi. This whip will provide us with everything. Whip, what is your duty?" asked the tortoise.

"To flog," replied the whip, and immediately it commenced to flog the tortoise and his family. The tortoise was very sorry he had locked the door and it was a long time before he could escape from the whip.

The next day, he determined to have his revenge, and took the whip to the king. He explained that it was as good as Ajayi's spoon and could work wonders. He presented the whip to the king. The king then summoned all the people to a great feast, and when they had gathered, he explained that Olokun had sent them another gift. Then turning to the whip he said, "What is your duty, whip?"

"To flog," replied the whip, and it commenced to flog everybody present including the king.

The tortoise had in the meantime concealed himself in a mortar in the corner of the king's compound and was safe. He greatly enjoyed the joke as the people ran around crying for help and trying to escape from the whip. At last the whip lay down and was still. The sore and angry people heard somebody laughing in the mortar and they went and dragged the tortoise out of his hiding place and took him before the king. He was promptly executed for his great impudence.

Why the Hawk Never Steals

There was once a couple who had been married a long time, but who had had no children. This was a great disappointment to them. The wife begged her husband to visit a certain pagan priest who was reported to be very clever and who possessed a very great juju.

So the man went and found the priest, and told him his story, and the priest promised to consult the juju and see what could be done. And in due course the woman gave birth to a baby girl. The man and his wife were both very happy and thankful, and they called the girl Alantere.

When the man went to thank the priest for his help, he was told that on no account must Alantere work, for this was the bargain the juju had made in return for sending the girl.

The man returned home and told his wife. But neither of them minded very much, because they were so thankful to have a child at last.

As Alantere grew up she was never allowed to do the work that daughters are expected to do in their fathers' compounds. Instead of drawing water, sweeping, or helping her mother to prepare the fufu, she would spend her time sleeping, eating, or going out to visit and talk with her friends. Thus it was that Alantere grew up to be a very lazy girl.

When Alantere was about eighteen years of age, her father married a second wife. This woman was very jealous and hated the girl because of her lazy ways. She had been told the reason why Alantere did not work, but she was not sympathetic. Then one day, when her husband and his first wife had gone out to visit friends and she and Alantere were left alone, her opportunity came to make Alantere help in the house. She beat the girl and made her sweep out the compound and prepare the food. When this was done, she sent her to the pool to fetch water. As the girl stooped over the water to fill her bucket, a strange thing happened. The goddess of the pool, Oluweri, rising to the surface, snatched the girl and drew her down into the depths of the water.

When Alantere's parents returned home there was no sign of their daughter, and they became worried. The second wife denied all knowledge of her whereabouts, and said that she had gone out. When Alantere did not return, her father collected his friends, telling them that Alantere had surely been stolen and that they must search for her. It was decided they should divide into groups and search in different parts of the bush, calling out her name all the time. Now it so happened that one of the searchers passed Oluweri's pool, and as he called out, Alantere appeared on the surface of the water. She was dressed in beautiful garments and jewelry, and looked like a queen; around her, floating on the surface of the water, were mats woven in gold and silver.

Alantere then sang to the man, and in her

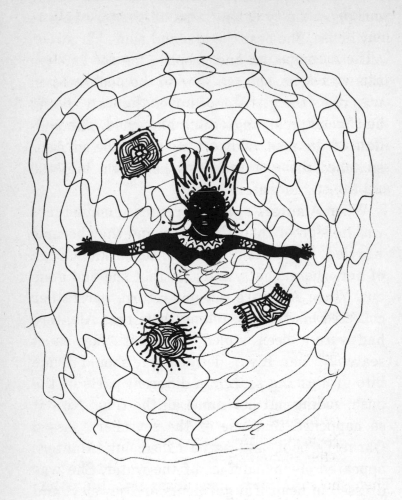

song she told him how she had been made to work by her stepmother, and what had befallen her.

The man was very surprised by what he had just witnessed and ran to find Alantere's parents. Her father and mother, together with all their friends, came quickly to the pool and called Alantere to come out from the water. As before, she came to the surface dressed in fine clothes and sang:

> Alantere, Alantere,
> The gods ordered her not to work.
> No duties can she perform, yet
> When her parents had gone
> She was beaten and made to work,
> Was set to fetch water from the pool,
> From Oluweri's own pool.
>
> Alantere, Alantere,
> Then suddenly came the goddess
> Of the stream, called Oluweri,
> Bore her down to the depths
> Of the pool to be seen no more,
> No more till they meet her beyond,
> After Oluweri's pool.

Then she sank back once again into the quiet waters.

Each time they came to the pool and called her name the same performance would take place,

207

but nobody could induce her to come away from Oluweri and her magic pool. Worried, the father then went to the old juju priest who had helped him over Alantere many years before, and told him the whole story of Alantere's misfortune. The priest first appealed to the juju himself, but without success, because the agreement that Alantere should do no work had been broken. The priest and the father then appealed to the gods to return Alantere, but they too refused to help in the matter. Appeals to Oluweri went unanswered.

The story of Alantere had now become common knowledge to everybody, and although people would come from time to time to offer their assistance in return for payment, nobody was able to help Alantere.

Then one day when Alantere's father was beginning to despair of ever being able to rescue his daughter from the clutches of Oluweri, a hawk came to him. The hawk had heard the story concerning Alantere and he said he was prepared to help the father. His charges, if he were successful, would be one coop of fowls. The father gladly promised to pay this, and together they set out for Oluweri's pool.

The hawk bade the father call his daughter while he hovered over the magic pool. When

Alantere reappeared, the hawk swooped down on her and caught her by the hair. Holding her lightly in his talons, he bore her up out of the water and carried her back to her father's house, setting her down gently within the compound.

There was great rejoicing and feasting and the hawk was thanked and congratulated on his success. Alantere's father presented the hawk not only with a coop of fowls, but with many more besides. The hawk told them that he was unable to carry all the fowls away as he had no place in which to keep them, but that if they had no objection he would leave them where they were and collect them one by one.

Since that day, the hawk has been coming for his fowls. He kills and collects them one by one. Nobody today knows how many Alantere's father gave him originally, but the hawk continues to come. That is why he never feels he is stealing when he snatches up a fowl from a farm.

The Bull and the Fly

Once, many years ago, there was a great famine in the Country of the Animals, and everybody was starving. The yam crop came to nothing, the groundnuts shriveled up, the plantains did not develop, and even the peppers and okra failed. The grass was burned, and the corn never came to a head.

Even the animals who lived on other animals went hungry, because those who lived on corn, crops, and plants were skinny and dry and hardly worth eating.

It was obvious to everybody that something would have to be done if they were not all to starve to death. The king of the animals, the lion, called a meeting of all animals, birds, fish, and insects, to see what should be done.

It was perfectly clear to everybody that the gods were angry and that somebody would have to be sacrificed to appease them, and so remove this trouble from the land.

Nobody, however, could agree on who should be sacrificed, so the king decided that as nobody was ready to volunteer for sacrifice the only satisfactory method was to draw lots, and choose the victim by this method.

They proceeded to do this, and the elephant was chosen and duly killed. With so much meat suddenly in front of them, everybody thought it was a pity to leave it in the bush, so it was next decided to appoint a butcher to divide up the elephant for a feast. This proved as difficult as trying to find a volunteer for the sacrifice. Everybody wanted to be appointed to the honorable post of Chief Butcher.

Again, the lion decided to settle the issue by drawing lots, and the bull was selected as Chief Butcher. The bull then set to work to portion out the elephant's meat amongst all the animals, birds, fish, and insects.

While the meat was being cut up, the fly, who was determined not to be forgotten, demanded his share. Now the bull disliked the fly and he replied, "Just keep your eyes on mine and I will not forget you, brother." The fly kept on looking at the bull's eyes until the whole of the meat had been shared out and nothing remained.

"What about my share of the sacrifice?" cried the fly.

The bull, who disliked and despised the fly more than ever, took no trouble to hide his feelings; he regarded the fly with contempt while he slowly flicked his tail. "My friend," he said, "you are of no importance. There is nothing for you, and, moreover, there is nothing you can do about it, except to go on looking at my eyes as I told you to do before."

Not unnaturally this made the fly very angry indeed, and he replied, "So be it; from this time onwards I and all my descendants will continue to look at your eyes and the eyes of your descendants forever."

This threat has been carried out, and this is

the reason why flies annoy cattle, and why cattle hate flies.

Even the most weak and despised are often capable of taking their revenge on the powerful and strong.

Olusegbe

A victorious Yoruba army had just defeated the Itsekiri people in a pitched battle. It was now moving slowly along the forest track towards its home town with its booty.

First came the laughing wives and some of the older children of the victorious soldiers; then followed the equally happy and laughing soldiers with their bows slung around their shoulders or their spears resting lightly at the slope. Next came the captured Itsekiri people themselves, not looking happy like the previous part of the procession. Here and there along the line marched a soldier to keep an eye on them, and to see that they did not try to run away, for they were all slaves.

Some were women. Most of them carried large wicker baskets or calabashes on their heads. These contained a rich assortment of goods, ceremonial robes, beads comprising *iyum, segi, okun, eyinla, esuru,* and a rich variety of booty. In the next part of the procession were the cattle of the defeated Itsekiris.

At a little distance behind and mounted on horseback, came the captains of the victorious army, and then behind these and alone rode the Yoruba general who had been responsible for the victory, Olusegbe.

Olusegbe was greatly respected by the Yorubas because he had never been defeated in battle during his period of command. His enemies had discovered that if they did not run away from him, they were either killed or captured.

Olusegbe was a lonely man, and one of his soldiers was talking about him as they marched

along. "I wonder if our general, Olusegbe, will choose a wife from among the captured Itsekiri women, for many of them are very beautiful."

"He has not even taken a wife from his own people yet. He is a strange man," replied his companion.

"It is said of him that he keeps a powerful juju in his compound, which is the reason for his continued success," replied the first soldier.

"I have heard that too," replied the second. And then the feasting and dancing that would occupy the night that lay ahead filled them with other thoughts, and they forgot about Olusegbe.

Olusegbe was thinking similar thoughts about himself as he rode along. He had taken a quick look at the captured Itsekiri women before they set out for home, but he had been dissatisfied with them all.

Soon the forest track led down to a river and the Yorubas and slaves crossed over. As Olusegbe reined in his horse on the bank to watch the procession crossing, his eyes caught sight of a green vegetable, callel *ewuro-odo,* growing on the river bank. He dismounted and picked it. Holding it up by one of its leaves he said aloud, "Ah, this is an exquisite vegetable—if it could become a man's wife how appreciated it would be."

Immediately, the vegetable fell from his hand,

and when it touched the ground it changed into a very beautiful maiden. Olusegbe fell in love with her and asked her to follow him home. The Vegetable Maiden bowed low to him, and followed quietly behind.

Olusegbe and the Vegetable Maiden crossed the river and as they walked up the bank on the farther side his eyes caught sight of a bird of bright and unusual plumage. "Ah," said Olusegbe again, "if only a man's wife could be like this beautiful bird." As he spoke his thoughts, the bird changed into a beautiful maiden and she followed him too.

After a little time, they came to a cool, clear stream and the day being hot, the general dismounted to refresh himself from the waters. "What cool, clear water—I have never tasted better—if only it were a beautiful woman instead of a stream." To Olusegbe's astonishment he suddenly found a third beautiful maiden standing in front of him with a calabash of water. He drank from her bowl, and handing it back said, "Follow me. Surely you too will be my wife." And the third woman followed him.

Olusegbe had continued on his way for some little distance when quite suddenly, a gazelle ran across the track. "Ah, what a fine animal," he remarked. As he spoke it seemed to change its mind and, running towards him, it changed

217

into a beautiful woman, and she followed him too.

When the general had nearly reached his town and was busy pondering over these strange occurrences, he noticed a very large and beautiful butterfly hovering near an awuusa nut, which grew on a nearby tree. It was a variety that he had never seen before.

Olusegbe laughed to himself and half in jest, said aloud, "I suppose if I said, 'Ah, what a beautiful butterfly,' and 'Ah, what a beautiful awuusa nut,' they would immediately turn into two beautiful maidens and wish to marry me and return to my home." Hardly had he spoken his thoughts before his remarks came true and now six very beautiful maidens followed behind his horse.

The people of the town were not surprised to see the six maidens following their general, thinking them to be some of the Itsekiri women. Olusegbe's soldiers and slaves were surprised, however, for the maidens had not been with the general when they all set out for home.

There were great celebrations that night and much feasting and dancing, and the booty was divided and the soldiers returned to their families and farms. As for Olusegbe, he married the six maidens and had his compound rebuilt and enlarged to accommodate them all. The Vegetable Maiden became his first wife, and Olusegbe was very fond of her. He preferred her to his other five wives.

One day the Vegetable Wife said, "Olusegbe, the people of this town say that your great powers as an army general are due to the fact that you keep a powerful juju, which prevents you from ever being defeated in battle. Is this true?"

Olusegbe replied, "I have never told anyone before, but now that I have married, and you are my senior wife, there is no harm in revealing my secret to you. Yes, my success is due to the presence of a juju. At the end of the compound you will see a jar of liquid and a broom that is never used for sweeping. When there is a danger of war or an attack, I take the broom and dip into the magic liquid. And then nobody can defeat me. However, you must tell nobody about this, for it is a secret that only the two of us share." The Vegetable Wife promised to tell nobody.

Not very long after this, as there was now peace in the land, Olusegbe asked the king for permission to leave his kingdom and travel abroad for some little time, as he wished to see an old friend of his who lived in a distant town. The king consented to Olusegbe's wishes, and a few days later the general set out on his travels, leaving the Vegetable Wife in charge of his home and his five other wives.

All went well for some time and then, quite suddenly and without any warning, a neighboring tribe attacked the town. The people had only sufficient time to close the city gates and man the walls, for the enemy had taken them by surprise. The king was very distressed that his best general should be absent at such a time, and feared the consequences of his absence.

Olusegbe's Vegetable Wife watched the battle from the town walls, and then going back to her house, she picked up Olusegbe's flute and played it while the other wives sang:

Olusegbe—Olusegbe, my husband,
Ablest general in all the land,
Remember the nut who followed as your wife,
The colored bird who sang in the tree,
And the butterfly who was close to the nut,
The gazelle who ran across your horse's path,
The green vegetable that by the river grew,
The waters of the stream, all your wives.
Now the war has reached the city wall,
O, Olusegbe, you are far away.

While the Vegetable Wife was playing to the other wives, she suddenly remembered Olusegbe's words about the magic liquid and the broom. Throwing down the flute, she ran to the bottom of the compound and picking up the broom, dipped it into the pot. Then she carried the broom to the senior captain defending the city walls and presented it to him. Presently the enemy were driven off from their attack with heavy losses, and they retired defeated to their own country.

Olusgbe, when he heard of the sudden attack on his town, hurried home. He was very pleased to find the enemy defeated and all well with his people, and even more pleased when the Vegetable Wife told him how she had used his juju during his absence to assist the senior captain.

Olusegbe stayed at home for two seasons, and then, when it seemed that all was peaceful, he again sought permission from the king to depart on another visit to his friend, and his request was granted.

The neighboring enemy had been waiting for Olusegbe to absent himself before renewing their attack, and their spies were quick to announce his departure. "We were unlucky last time, but our only hope will be to attack when Olusegbe is not at home," they thought to themselves.

With sudden fury, they threw themselves upon the town, but the Vegetable Wife was ready this time and dipped the broom into the liquid juju and ran with it to the captain in charge during Olusegbe's absence. This time the enemy, in spite of their initial advantage of a surprise attack, suffered more heavily from the defenders, and were driven off with such great losses that finally they broke in utter confusion and disorder and never again considered attacking Olusegbe's town.

Not very long after Olusegbe's return, the king died and a new king was chosen in his place. It was the custom in those days among the Yorubas for the general to call on the new ruler, and for him and the chiefs to ask the new ruler upon whom he considered that they should wage war. Olusegbe made the inquiry and the king's counselors were all very surprised when told it should be the Country of the Frogs. It was the king's wish, however, and as such would have to be carried out. Apparently, when the new ruler had been a little boy, a large frog had spat in his eye, and he had never forgiven the frogs for this.

Olusegbe assembled all the army captains to a meeting to discuss with them the best means of waging war on the frogs. While this meeting was taking place, Olusegbe and his officers were overheard by a small ant, who ran off as fast as his tiny legs would carry him to warn the frogs of the new king's wishes and plans. Not unnaturally, this caused great fear and consternation among the frogs.

One of the wisest of their community, an old bullfrog, stood up and said, "My friends, now that our good friend the ant has given us timely warning, we must plan carefully. We have plenty of time to think of ways of defending ourselves. I suggest that we approach that very wise animal the tortoise with a view to enlisting his help in our difficulties. Even if he cannot help us, he will at least give us good counsel."

So the bullfrog was sent to call on the tortoise and explain matters. The tortoise listened carefully.

"Alas, I can see little hope for the frogs if they are forced to fight Olusegbe, for he has never lost a battle, and because of his juju he cannot be defeated by anybody."

"What is this juju?" asked the bullfrog.

"During the time Olusegbe's town was last attacked, I happened to be staying in the town and living close to the general's compound. I also happened to overhear the woman he calls his Vegetable Wife speaking to the others about the general's juju saving the town. She went to the corner of the compound and taking an old broom, dipped it into some strange-looking liquid that is kept there in a pot. Then she ran with the broom to the captain in charge."

"Do you think the liquid and broom were Olusegbe's juju?" asked the bullfrog.

"I am sure of it, my friend. Now it seems obvious to me that the only course open to you frogs is to bribe the woman known as the Vegetable Wife, and get her to give you the broom and the pot of liquid. Having secured these, we will see how Olusegbe's forces fare."

The bullfrog thanked the tortoise for his information and returned to the frogs' council, and related to them all that the tortoise had said.

It was decided to muster all the young frogs and to tax every frog to the extent of one cowrie shell per head to pay the bribe to the Vegetable Wife of Olusegbe.

When the money had been collected, and it was a very considerable sum, and the old bullfrog had further purchased a jar of honey and taken a certain percentage of the funds for himself and the tortoise, he set out for Olusegbe's compound. Hopping up to the Vegetable Wife, he greeted her respectfully and told her how very beautiful she looked and how he envied Olusegbe for having such a lovely wife. The Vegetable Wife was very flattered by these words; then the bullfrog presented her with the jar of honey. She knew nothing of the new king's intended war on the frogs, suspecting nothing.

225

When the bullfrog had made friends with her, he asked if he might borrow the pot of liquid and broom for a little while. He said that he would return it without fail the following day. At first the Vegetable Wife refused his request, but when she saw all the bags of cowrie shells he offered her as security, she finally agreed to his wishes, provided he promised to return them before her husband noticed their loss. So the bullfrog removed the pot and broom and, with the help of the tortoise, hid them in the forest.

The following morning, while Olusegbe was making preparations to commence war, the frogs attacked the town in their thousands. They came on like a moving sea, climbing the walls and overrunning the town and killing a lot of people, including the new king, who had been responsible for the war. Olusegbe's army were incapable of fighting so many frogs, and seeing the battle was going against him, he ran to his compound to find the juju. "Where is my juju?" he demanded of the Vegetable Wife. Full of grief for her foolish action, she told Olusegbe the story of the bullfrog and his presents of the honey and the cowrie shells. Olusegbe was very angry, but he had no time to quarrel with his wife; the frogs were already approaching the compound and he returned to fight with his remaining soldiers. For the first time in his life

Olusegbe was defeated in battle. That night the town had fallen and the frogs had taken possession of everything. "My share," croaked the bullfrog, who had played such a large part in the victory, "is the six beautiful wives of Olusegbe —he will have no further use for them. I will go and pay my respects to my Vegetable Wife and inspect my house." He hopped off from the market place.

When he arrived at what had once been Olusegbe's house, he found the six wives weeping and wringing their hands in grief.

"Why such a sad scene? That is no way to welcome your new husband to his house," he croaked. "Go and prepare food, for I am tired after the day's fighting and want to rest tonight."

"Where is our husband, Olusegbe?" cried the six wives.

"Your husband Olusegbe is dead, and you can forget about him. I am your husband now and you will obey me. Go and fetch my food, and stop making this horrid noise. I do not like it," he ordered, puffing himself out and trying to look important. The frog's absurd appearance had the opposite effect of what he desired, for the wives laughed at him, and then the Vegetable Wife began to sing softly to herself, and the other wives joined in:

Olusegbe, Olusegbe, you are dead.
The fairest of all maidens, your wives,
They are six in number.
Green vegetable that by the river grew,
The colored bird who sang on the tree,
The waters of the stream.
Then the nut who followed as your wife,
And the butterfly close to the nut.
Gazelle, who crossed the path.
We return to the place we come from
Back to riverside and forest cool,
Olusegbe, fare you well.

When the wives had finished their song, they vanished and the bullfrog found himself alone in the compound. He remained motionless for a long time, staring ahead, only his shiny sides moving quickly as he breathed. "Very strange," he said to himself. "Very strange indeed."

Olusegbe was not dead, however, for after having been defeated by the frogs and driven out of the town with his army, full of shame at the disgrace, he called one of his captains to him and asked the man to kill him with his own sword. The captain, however, refused, saying that all was not lost, and if Olusegbe could only find out who had removed the juju, they might yet manage to retake the town and punish the frogs.

Olusegbe decided after some time to try this,

so saying good-bye to his men, he set out alone to find out what had happened.

Olusegbe wandered about the forest by himself for a very long time. Then one day he met a leopard.

"Are you not Olusegbe, the great general?" the leopard asked.

"I am, or perhaps I should say I was," replied Olusegbe.

"The animals say," went on the leopard, "that you seek the one who was responsible for your defeat. If you listen carefully, Olusegbe, I will help you. You must know that when you spoke with your captains, your plans were overheard by an ant. The ant went and told the frogs, and an old bullfrog who, incidentally, now dwells in your house, suggested to his friends that they should consult the tortoise. Olusegbe, it is the tortoise who was responsible for your defeat more than anybody else, for he suggested to the bullfrog that the only way to overcome you was to bribe your Vegetable Wife with honey and cowries to give up your juju. This, as you well know, she did, and the tortoise knows the place where the frog hid your juju. If you could only capture the tortoise, I think you might be able to recover your former power."

"Cursed be the tortoise and all his children,

and may he be looked upon as the weakest and most irresponsible of all animals," said Olusegbe. "I will seek him out and kill him."

"No," said the leopard. "I will do that. He is an enemy of mine."

"Why do you dislike the tortoise so much?" asked Olusegbe.

"Not so long ago there arose a quarrel between us over quite a small matter. I will not trouble you with the details of our quarrel, but I now know him to be a very cunning and crafty animal. One day, there came to my house an *alabe*[1] who said he would like to put the tribal markings on my children. I was agreeable to this idea and my children were called and prepared for the ceremony and operation. When we were all ready to commence, however, the *alabe* announced that he was unable to perform in front of grownups. He asked me to go away and leave him alone with my children. This I did, and they were left together in a room in my house. I waited a very long time and then growing restless, I entered to see what was keeping them so long. It was then that I perceived the reason for the long silence. All my children had been murdered by the *alabe* and he had fled. I went after him, but could not find him, and it was not

[1] *alabe*—native doctor, who is responsible for tribal markings and circumcisions.

230

long before I discovered that the murdering *alabe* and the tortoise were one and the same person. Now I have at long last a clue to the whereabouts of the tortoise, and I will never rest until I have revenged the murder of my children."

Olusegbe thanked the leopard for his help and continued on his wanderings. The leopard had discovered the tortoise was resting at a certain house near a ferry, and so he set off for the place. The tortoise, however, was warned, and rushing out of the house, he called on the ferry men to carry him away.

There were two paddles with the canoe. The forward paddler was practically deaf and the aft was totally blind. The tortoise scrambled into the canoe as fast as his tiny legs could carry him, screaming to the blind man to paddle away from the shore, and waving frantically to the deaf man to go out into midstream. It seemed to the tortoise as if they would never get away from the bank. Then at last they were clear and set off paddling downstream. At this stage, the leopard suddenly appeared on the bank, roaring and calling to them to come back. When they took no notice, he hired another canoe and went in pursuit, shouting to the paddlers ahead to stop. The blind paddler in the rear called the tortoise's attention to the fact that somebody was calling on them to stop, but the tortoise asked the deaf man if he heard anything, and when the man replied that he did not, the tortoise urged them on to further efforts with a promise of a big present at the end of the journey. All the while the leopard's canoe was slowly gaining on them, and noticing this, the tortoise ordered his paddlers to make for the bank. The only hope now was to hide in the bush before the leopard caught up with them. Unfortunately for the tortoise, the canoe was caught up the next minute in a mangrove tree and it immediately capsized. It was at this stage that the leopard jumped out of his canoe and swam up to the struggling tortoise, who was trying to hide himself among the roots of the mangrove tree.

The tortoise kept his head. Only a battle of wits with the leopard could save him now. The leopard was trying to get hold of his legs under the water. A few seconds later he had gripped one of the tortoise's legs.

The tortoise laughed and sang:

> Leopard, you have caught a root of the mangrove,
> It is nothing to me—I am as safe as ever.

The leopard promptly let go. Plunging around

in the water, and wishing he had the tortoise
for only a minute on dry land, he caught hold
of a root of mangrove. Perceiving this, the tortoise sang:

> He has caught me. He has caught me.
> Oh, I am dead and finished.

So they went on for a long time. Whenever the
leopard caught hold of the tortoise, that wise
animal would pretend he was free—when the
leopard caught hold of the mangrove roots, the
tortoise pretended he was holding his leg.

They might have gone on for a long time like
this, had not a passing fish come to help the leopard when he had at last caught hold of the
tortoise's leg. The animal who had caused so
much trouble was then dragged ashore, and
brought as a prisoner before Olusegbe.

The tortoise begged Olusegbe to save his life.

"Where is my juju?" demanded Olusegbe. The
tortoise told him, and the general lost no time
in regaining it from where the bullfrog had
hidden it in the bush. First Olusegbe collected his
people and soldiers about him and when they
had all gathered together, he offered a sacrifice
to the gods and asked for their help. Their prayers were answered, for the gods sent down a
plague of snakes and the frog-eating birds called

ehuru. In a few days the town had been cleared of the frogs. Many of them perished, including the old bullfrog who had taken possession of Olusegbe's compound. Then, as quickly as they had come, the snakes and *ehuru* birds disappeared. So ended the frogs' conquest.

The victorious Yoruba people were again moving slowly along the same forest track that they had passed some years before, after they had defeated the Itsekiri people in battle.

First came their newly elected king, Olusegbe, followed by the laughing and happy men, women, and children carrying their loads. They were all returning to their homes. Next in the procession came the leopard and close by the tortoise, now a prisoner and carrying the pot of magic liquid and the broom, Olusegbe's juju.

Olusegbe was a lonely man, and one of his soldiers was talking about him as they marched along. "I wonder if our king, Olusegbe, will find his six wives again, for they were very beautiful."

"He is a strange man," replied his companion.

"It is possible that his powerful juju will assist him," repeated the first soldier. "That is possible," answered the second man.

Olusegbe as he rode along, was thinking similar thoughts about himself. He had searched everywhere for his wives, but had not seen them.

Soon the forest track led down to the river, and the Yorubas, the leopard, and the tortoise crossed over. As Olusegbe reined in his horse on the bank to watch the procession crossing, his eyes caught sight of a green vegetable called *ewuro-odo* growing on the river bank. He dismounted and picked it. Holding it up by one of its leaves, he said aloud, "Ah, this is a very beautiful vegetable! If it could only be like my Vegetable Wife, how appreciated it would be." Immediately it fell from his hands, and when it touched the ground it changed into Olusegbe's first wife. The Vegetable Wife bowed to him and asked his forgiveness for having parted with his juju.

Olusegbe and his first wife crossed the river, and as they walked up the bank on the farther side, his eyes caught sight of a bird of bright and unusual plumage. "Ah," said Olusegbe again, "if this beautiful bird could only be like my second wife, how happy I should be." As he spoke his thoughts, the bird changed suddenly, and so he found his second wife.

Everything happened as before. They came to the cool, clear stream and his third wife came forth when he refreshed himself. Then the gazelle ran across his path and turned back into his fourth wife, and later he came to the beautiful butterfly and the awuusa nut, and so retrieved all his six wives.

The people of the town were pleased to see the six maidens again and welcomed them back. There was great celebration that night and much feasting and dancing, and the people returned to their homes and farms. As for Olusegbe, he was a very popular king and was very fond of his six wives, and they bore him many children, and there was great peace in the land.

As for the tortoise, Olusegbe handed him over to the leopard who brought him before the king of the animals, and charged him with murdering his children while disguised as an *alabe*. He was sentenced to die. They decided to suffocate him by sewing him up in a bag of corn. The tortoise, however, would not die, so the wise elders of the king of the animals suggested that the tortoise be taken to the top of a high mountain and dashed to pieces. The leopard took him up to the mountaintop in his mouth and dropped him over the side. And so perished the tortoise for his mischief-making.

The Story of Stranger and Traveler

A very long time ago all cats and dogs were friends. Then they quarreled. The quarrel was so severe that the king and the gods were never able to settle it, and it has continued ever since.

It all started when a certain dog and cat decided to go on and visit a strange land that they had heard about. "My friend, if we reach this strange land, we must not disclose our names to the people. I will call myself 'Stranger' and you will be 'Traveler,'" said the cat. The dog thought this a very good idea. He usually agreed with the cat over everything because he felt that the cat was a very intelligent animal.

Their wanderings led them finally to the country of the Yorubas, and arriving at a certain town, the cat and dog went to call on the local chief to pay their respects. They were invited to stay and accommodation was provided for them by their chief. When they were asked what their names were they replied, "Stranger" and

"Traveler." The chief was a little deaf and he understood them to say one was a stranger and the other was a traveler. He did not realize that these were their names.

Now there was an ancient custom among the Yorubas at that time that food would always be prepared and given to strangers, but travelers were not provided for and were expected to feed themselves. The result of this was that the chief's people brought food to Stranger, the cat, and poor Traveler, the dog, went without. The dog was very angry and went to the quarters of the cat and suggested that they should leave Yoruba country and return to their own land.

So Stranger and Traveler packed their loads and went to pay their respects to the chief, who, on finding they were departing for their country, presented them with a fine cow.

"I suggest we take this fine cow home to our country," said Stranger.

"No," replied Traveler, "while we have been here you have had plenty to eat and I am starving. We will kill it now and divide it equally between us."

"All right, we will kill it then. I have a knife with me and we can cut it up," replied Stranger. Traveler had no knife, so Stranger killed and cut up the cow.

"How do you suggest we divide the cow?" asked Traveler, as he watched Stranger work.

"I suggest that any portion of the cow which makes a noise against the knife goes to you, and any that does not is mine," replied Stranger. So in this way the cow was divided up and shared out, all the meat of course going to the cat and all the bones to the dog. Traveler was very hungry by this time and he set to work to crunch up the bones, and greatly enjoyed them. And dogs have enjoyed eating bones ever since that day.

When Stranger had finished dividing up the cow, he felt that the share out had not been very fair, so he presented the cow's head to Traveler too. Traveler had by this time eaten all the bones, so he picked up the cow's head and said, "As you have a lot of meat to carry, Stranger, I will not wait. I am going on quickly and will see you later." So he trotted off with the cow's head. After they had spent most of the day on the road, Traveler began to feel tired. Coming to a great tree whose branches shaded the road, he sat down to rest. As he lay down panting and looking at the cow's head, an idea suddenly occurred to Traveler. He thought that instead of carrying the head any farther, he would bury it in the ground and collect it later. When he had rested, Traveler set to work with his front paws and soon had a hole scratched in the ground. Then he proceeded to bury the cow's head and scratch the earth back again. Now it so happened that he covered every portion with earth except the cow's two eyes. These were left protruding out of the ground. Satisfied, Traveler continued on his way till he reached home.

Stranger traveled slowly because of his great load of meat. At last he too reached the cool shade of the tree, and sat down to rest. As he lay stretched out, he suddenly caught sight of two eyes looking at him from the ground close by. He sprang up with a scream and all his hair

stood up along the ridge of his spine. The eyes
continued to stare at him and he was very
frightened. He did not realize that they were
the eyes of the cow's head Traveler had buried.
He thought the earth was taking him to task
for owning so great a share of the cow, and to
save himself from any evil jujus he sang:

> O Mother Earth, are these your eyes?
> Do you want me to put down all my flesh?
> And run away without taking any.
> Oh please spare my life, Mother Earth,
> And all the cow's meat shall be yours.

There was no reply to Stranger's song so he decided to leave the meat behind as an offering
to Mother Earth, and go home empty-handed.

The next day Traveler returned to the tree
to collect the cow's head, and he was surprised
to find the rest of the cow lying close by. He dug
up the head and took it home, together with the
rest of the flesh.

He had not returned very long before
Stranger came to call on him and related the
terrible story of how Mother Earth's eyes had
watched him from the ground while he rested
under the tree. Stranger had hardly finished
telling his story when he suddenly stopped. He
was gazing very intently over Traveler's tail.
Traveler turned round to look. Stranger was

gazing at the cow's head and the large pile of flesh that lay close by.

"Where did you get all that flesh from, Traveler?" he asked.

"From Mother Earth," replied Traveler with a great laugh.

This was where their friendship ended. They quarreled violently, each claiming the cow's flesh as his own. The quarrel was taken to the king, but he was unable to settle it. Then the quarrel was taken to the gods, but they failed to settle matters either. Since that day all cats and dogs have been enemies. Whenever they meet, the cats will arch their backs, trying to describe the large amount of cow's flesh that was stolen from Stranger, and the dogs will start to bark and shout as Traveler once did.

The Hunter and His Magic Flute

There once lived a mighty hunter called Ojo, and it was his custom, like all Yoruba hunters, to go off into the forest for long periods, sometimes for as much as three months. Ojo used to build a camp for himself with sticks and palm fronds in the center of the area he had chosen to hunt. He then set out each day with his bow and arrows for a day's hunting, returning later with the day's kill to the forest camp. Before settling down to sleep for the night, Ojo used to cut up the flesh and dry it over a fire. The camp served as a store as well as a place of refuge at night. When his store of dried flesh was sufficient, Ojo returned home to his wife, and she sold the dried meat to the villagers in exchange for their daily requirements.

Ojo had three dogs and he had given them strange names: "Cut to Pieces," "Swallow Up," and "Clear the Remains." His other possession was a very old flute, which Ojo claimed possessed very great magical powers. "For," said Ojo, "however far I go when hunting in the forest, if I blow on this flute 'Cut to Pieces,' 'Swallow Up,' and 'Clear the Remains,' will hear it and come to wherever I am."

When the next time came for Ojo to set out on his long hunting expedition, he decided to leave the three dogs behind, tied up with stout ropes in his compound. He asked his wife to look after them and, if they suddenly showed signs of great nervousness and agitation, to release them immediately and let them follow him to the forest. His wife having agreed, Ojo set out.

After three days' journey, Ojo came to the

place in the forest where he had decided to build his camp. He had never been in that region before, and, as far as he knew, none of the other hunters had been there either, but his experienced eyes and ears told him that the thick forest he now found himself in was full of game.

Ojo set to work and soon his camp was taking shape. However, for some reason or other Ojo felt worried. He had the feeling that all the time he was being watched, not by animals, but by some powerful evil spirit. When he was a boy he had often been told about the spirits of the forest, and he was afraid of them, although he had never seen any of them during all the years he had been hunting. Other hunters had claimed to have seen them; they had even seen the great Mother of the Forest, Iyabomba herself. Iyabomba, they had told him, was the size of ten full-grown men and her body was covered with hungry mouths.

When Ojo had completed his camp, he lay down inside to watch; the feeling of fear and of being watched never left him. He had the impression that something evil was drawing nearer to him and so Ojo was not altogether surprised when a huge monster suddenly appeared before him. Ojo immediately recognized it as the Mother of the Forest. The great Iyabomba stood before him. Ojo was too sick with fear to run away, he just stood rooted to the ground gazing at Iyabomba.

Suddenly, Iyabomba was speaking to him, "Have no fear, hunter. I know why you come to my domain and I will not devour you if you do me no harm." Then the Mother of the Forest departed as suddenly as she had come.

It was time for Ojo to hunt and he was more than thankful to get away from the terrifying Iyabomba. "Can Iyabomba's promise be relied on?" he asked himself. Ojo had a successful day's hunting, and when he returned later to his camp with the day's kill, his fear of the Mother of the Forest had abated. Ojo set to work to cut up the meat and then to light a fire and dry it. Afterwards he prepared his own meal and then settled down for a night's rest.

The following day, Ojo set off to hunt again. It was another successful day for him and he returned once again to his forest camp laden with meat. As he approached, the hunter was quick to notice that there had been a visitor to his camp during his absence. It did not require the expert eye of a hunter to recognize the great foot marks of Iyabomba in the grass, and when Ojo entered his hut, he found she had taken all the meat he had prepared the day before.

"Never mind," thought Ojo to himself, "I have had a good day's hunting and now perhaps the Mother of the Forest is satisfied." So he prepared the meat as before.

Iyabomba was not satisfied, however, for each time Ojo returned he found that she had stolen all that he had killed the previous day. The hunter was afraid to inquire from her why she took his meat, in case she ate him too, but after the sixth day Ojo still had nothing to show for all his skillful hunting. What annoyed Ojo still more was the fact that it was the best area in which he had ever hunted and it was all a waste of time because of Iyabomba's greed. "If I stay here for a year, the old hag will still continue to steal my meat," he thought to himself. Ojo did not go hunting the following day, instead he moved his camp to a distant part of the forest and commenced his work all over again. Here he was no more successful than before, for Iyabomba had followed him and continued to steal his meat. At last Ojo's anger overcame his fear and he decided to remain behind in his camp and wait for Iyabomba to come. She did not come all that day, however, so at last Ojo struck his camp and tied up all his loads. As he was departing Ojo called out in a loud tone, "Why have you eaten all my meat, you old hag?

Do you steal from every poor hunter who enters your forest?" Hardly had he spoken these words when there was an angry roar from Iyabomba and she came crashing through the forest towards him with all her mouths open as if to devour him. Ojo took to his heels and fled. Now Iyabomba was calling him with all her mouths to come back and be eaten, but Ojo ran faster. It was no use. She was much bigger than he and could have soon outpaced him long before he was clear of the forest. Seeing a great tree, Ojo hurriedly climbed up into its topmost branches as the Mother of the Forest came rushing up.

Not being able to climb up, she set to work with her great mouths and started to tear the bottom of the tree away, piece by piece. It was then that Ojo remembered his magic flute, which still hung from his shoulder. Picking it up, he blew a tune on it. Far away in his compound, "Cut to Pieces," "Swallow Up," and "Clear the Remains" heard the sounds and commenced to howl. Before Ojo's wife had time to release them, the dogs had snapped the ropes that tied them, and with one great leap they had cleared the mud walls of the compound and were racing towards Ojo.

In the meantime, however, Iyabomba was eating her way through the tree with great rapidity. Ojo waited until she had nearly eaten through and it was beginning to sway. Then, taking a small leather packet, which contained a fine magic powder, he sprinkled it on the tree and immediately it became whole again. Iyabomba was very surprised. She stopped and looked up at Ojo; then, turning another part of her body towards the tree she attacked it with her many mouths again. Each time the tree was nearly cut through Ojo sprinkled a little more of the magic powder on the tree and it immediately became whole again. In this way Ojo and Iyabomba continued for a long time, until at last all the magic powder had been used up, and the tree was nearly cut through again.

Ojo was beginning to think that his battle with the Mother of the Forest was nearly finished when to his great relief, "Cut to Pieces," "Swallow Up," and "Clear the Remains" suddenly appeared, and with a great noise, they threw themselves onto Iyabomba. There was a long and bitter fight, but at last they killed her and the three dogs, living up to their strange names, devoured everything that had once been the Mother of the Forest.

Ojo then climbed down the tree, and collecting up his things and his three dogs, he was about to return home and relate all these strange happenings to his wife when, greatly to his surprise, for they were in a very desolate spot, he saw a very beautiful woman standing close by.

"I have been held a prisoner by Iyabomba: now that you have killed her and rescued me, will you take me home, Ojo, and let me become your wife?" she asked the hunter.

Ojo was surprised that this beautiful woman should know his name, but he gladly consented to take her back with him and marry her. When they reached home Ojo's wife was very pleased to see them all, and there was great feasting and celebrations when the village were told that the Mother of the Forest was dead and that this beautiful woman, who was to become Ojo's second wife, had been rescued from the clutches of Iyabomba.

That night, when all was quiet and the people had returned home to sleep, a strange thing happened. Ojo's second wife, who had pretended to sleep, suddenly got up and commenced to change herself into a great creature with many mouths. She was in actual fact the sister of Iyabomba and had witnessed the killing of her sister by the hunter's dogs. She had made up her mind to revenge her sister's death and had changed herself into a beautiful woman as a disguise, knowing that Ojo would never suspect her, and would take her home with him. Now the time for her revenge had come. She would kill the hunter, his wife and their three dogs, and then return to rule in the place of her sister, as Mother of the Forest.

"Cut to Pieces," "Swallow Up," and "Clear the Remains" were in the compound. They sensed the change that was taking place inside the house and started to bark. This barking woke Ojo and his wife and before Iyabomba's sister could kill the hunter, they had rushed into the house and torn her to pieces too.

Thus perished Iyabomba, the Mother of the Forest, and her sister. Ojo often went to hunt afterwards in that part of the forest where he had first met Iyabomba, but he was never again disturbed by forest spirits and always returned from his hunting expeditions fully laden.

He lived with his wife, "Cut to Pieces," "Swallow Up," "Clear the Remains," and the magic flute, but he never took to himself a second wife.

Olobun's Sacrifice

Very long ago, there was a frog who possessed a very powerful juju. One day he went to market and hid under a tree and then began to sing:

Beautiful nuts, beautiful nuts,
Your place is in the farm, but here
In the market you are being
Prepared for food. Yes, for my food.
I come to market with juju,
And all you people who sell nuts
Will run away and I shall eat.

Sure enough, as he sang his song, everybody ran away, leaving their goods behind, for they were unable to combat the frog's juju. Then the frog helped himself to what he wanted and departed. The frog did this many times, always with the same results. The market people were terribly angry, and soon the trade of the whole town was disrupted and the townspeople suffered. They tried everything they could think of to combat the artful frog. Great warriors

were sent for, but they failed to kill the frog. Great hunters came next, and they failed to catch the frog. Next the juju doctors tried, but their juju was not as powerful as that of the frog, and so the mischief continued.

Then one day, when everybody was in despair, an old man arrived in the town. "I will catch the singer for you," he announced. He then set to work and carved an image of a standing figure with a pot arranged between its hands. In the pot he placed a lot of groundnuts, and then he carried the image out and placed it in the middle of the market. Next, taking a pot of gum, he coated the image and the groundnuts with the sticky liquid.

When next the frog came and sang his song, all the people, including the old man, ran away as usual, and when the frog was alone, he hopped about the deserted marketplace taking what he fancied. Soon he discovered the image. It was new, and he was very curious. Hopping up, he bowed low to the statue and with mocking politeness he said, "Good day, sir." There was no answer. "Can't you speak?" continued the frog. The frog then lost interest in the image. He was now wondering what the image kept in the pot between its wooden hands. Raising himself up on his webbed feet and resting his forelegs on the sides of the pot, he gazed inside. Suddenly he found that his forelegs had stuck fast to the sides of the pot. The frog struggled, and tried to free himself by pressing with his hind legs, but these too stuck fast when they came in contact with the gum. And so the frog remained stretched out and stuck fast, a sorry and ridiculous sight, and the people returned and killed him. The old man then suggested that the dead frog's flesh should be taken and sacrificed to Olobun.

The flesh and bones of the frog were placed in a pot and the old man prepared some liquid which he poured on top. When this ceremony was completed, a lizard was ordered to place the pot on his head and carry it to Olobun. So ended the trouble for the market people, and they were never again annoyed by frogs with jujus. As for the unfortunate lizard, it was the beginning of his misfortunes, for as he carried the pot to Olobun on his head, some of the liquid spilled and ran down his face. He tried to lick it off, it tasted very sweet and not unlike honey, and the lizard liked it. So, when nobody was looking he put down the pot, and taking up one of the frog's bones, he dipped it into the liquid and licked off the sweet stuff. The next minute the bone had slipped from his hand and stuck in his throat. The lizard tried and tried to get it to move up or down, but it had stuck tight, and

there it has remained ever since. That is why you will often see lizards jerking their heads up and down, for Olobun never forgave the lizard for tampering with his sacrifice.

1 2 3 4 5 75 74 73 72 71